*Optimum
Seeking
Methods*

PRENTICE-HALL INTERNATIONAL SERIES
IN THE PHYSICAL AND CHEMICAL ENGINEERING SCIENCES

NEAL R. AMUNDSON, EDITOR, *University of Minnesota*

ADVISORY EDITORS

ANDREAS ACRIVOS, *Stanford University*
MICHEL BOUDART, *University of California*
THOMAS J. HANRATTY, *University of Illinois*
DAVID E. LAMB, *University of Delaware*
JOHN M. PRAUSNITZ, *University of California*
L. E. SCRIVEN, *University of Minnesota*

ARIS *Vectors, Tensors, and the Basic Equations of Fluid Mechanics*
FREDRICKSON *Principles and Applications of Rheology*
HOLLAND *Multicomponent Distillation*
LEVICH *Physiochemical Hydrodynamics*
LYKOV AND MIKHAYLOV *Theory of Energy and Mass Transfer*
WILDE *Optimum Seeking Methods*

PRENTICE-HALL, INC.
PRENTICE-HALL INTERNATIONAL, UNITED KINGDOM, AND EIRE
PRENTICE-HALL OF CANADA, LTD., CANADA

Optimum Seeking Methods

DOUGLASS J. WILDE

*Department of
Chemical Engineering
Stanford University*

PRENTICE-HALL, INC.

Englewood Cliffs, N.J.

PRENTICE-HALL INTERNATIONAL, INC., *London*
PRENTICE-HALL OF AUSTRALIA, PTY., LTD., *Sydney*
PRENTICE-HALL OF CANADA, LTD., *Toronto*
PRENTICE-HALL FRANCE, S.A.R.L., *Paris*
PRENTICE-HALL OF INDIA (PRIVATE) LIMITED, *New Delhi*
PRENTICE-HALL OF JAPAN, INC., *Tokyo*
PRENTICE-HALL DE MEXICO S.A., *Mexico City*

Library of Congress Catalog Card Number 63-20039

Printed in the United States of America
63823 C

To

Mrs. Charles T. Wilde, *mother*
Miss Marie Waters, *English teacher*
Mr. Ed Wilson, *engineer*
Professor Andreas Acrivos, *scholar*

Preface

Although this book is based primarily on the work of statisticians, the author is a chemical engineer. This may suggest the interdisciplinary character of the work, which hopefully is broad enough in viewpoint to interest not only engineers and statisticians, but economists, applied mathematicians, operations analysts, and behavioral scientists as well.

Optimization—finding the best way to do things—is obviously of interest in the practical world of production, trade, and politics, where small changes in efficiency can spell the difference between success or disaster for any enterprise, be it neighborhood store, mammoth industrial complex, or governing political party. Today as always many important decisions are made simply by describing the system under study as precisely and quantitatively as possible, selecting some measure of system effectiveness, and then seeking the state of the system which gives the most desirable value of this criterion. Since description and understanding of systems is the traditional task of the engineers, economists, and other applied scientists for whom this book is written, it would be presumptious to discuss such a broad topic in this brief work. Moreover, choosing a measure of effectiveness is in most cases either completely obvious or so clouded by nonquantitative value judgments as to be extremely difficult, and so we do not deal with this delicate question either. Instead we concentrate entirely on the technical problems associated with the process of optimization itself.

Over a span of almost two centuries, the only mathematical methods known for handling optimization problems were the classical differential and variational calculus. With the rise of "operations research" since the Second World War, there has been renewed interest in optimization methods for dealing with problems not solvable by classical methods. Many of these techniques—linear and dynamic programming, for instance—have already been extensively described in technical books. However, a search for the optimum of a function more or less unknown to the observer necessarily involves experimentation, for the only way to gain information about such a function is by direct measurement. For this reason we have given the name *optimum seeking procedures* to the strategies guiding search for the optimum of any function about which full knowledge is not available. Such functions arise not only in situations where direct observations must be made on a physical or economic system, but also in theoretical studies where the mathematical form of the criterion of effectiveness is so complicated that it can only be evaluated directly on a high speed computer.

This book is based on material presented to senior engineering students whose mathematical training comprised only standard calculus courses, and anyone who can take a partial derivative should be also to follow our exposition. Indeed, the development depends very little on the calculus, the mathematics being rather simple, although probably a bit unfamiliar to engineers and economists. The book is intended not only as a text for undergraduate science students, but also as a reference book for practicing economists, engineers, and statisticians who may not have been able to keep up with the rapid development of experimental optimization techniques.

Problems in experimental optimization are good vehicles for learning about logic, multidimensional geometry, and elementary probability theory. As consequences of the technical treatment certain general decision principles are developed which may be useful even when there is no time for detailed and rigorous analysis. For example, study of experimental optimization problems involving a single independent variable gives insight into the important minimax concept as well as the somewhat startling technique of randomization. Close examination of multivariable problems unearths some rather disturbing facts about graphical reasoning and the paradoxes that can arise from failing to realize that even engineers and economists often must work with non-Euclidean space. Analysis of interactions between variables shows how one may blunder onto a false optimum—one which appears optimal but really isn't. Stochastic approximation theory illustrates just how experimental error can slow down a search. It also indicates how one might weight new observations with old ones to improve operations. As might be expected, changes should be more and more gradual as experience is gained, and the harmonic sequence $1, \frac{1}{2}, \frac{1}{3}, \frac{1}{4}, \ldots$ turns out to be particularly significant in weighting successive observations to cancel out random errors.

The style of presentation has been greatly influenced by the ideas of G. Polya of Stanford University in his books *How to Solve it* and *The*

Mathematics of Plausible Inference. Thus we have tried to show how the originators of the techniques discussed might have discovered them. As Polya suggests, this approach, while requiring more words than a formal proof, helps develop creativity in the student. We have found that presenting the material this way has in fact stimulated students to original and valuable ideas, and it is a pleasure to acknowledge here the contributions of undergraduates Roger Ben Haïm at the Ecole Nationale Supérieure des Industries Chimiques, Nancy, France, and of Leaton T. Oliver and Rafael B. Cruz-Diaz at the University of Texas. While acknowledging the help of others, let us thank Professors J. Kiefer of Cornell University, Thomas E. Corrigan of Ohio State, Irving F. Miller of the Polytechnic Institute of Brooklyn, and William A. Graves of Colorado State, who have caught several mistakes and suggested better methods of presentation. Particular credit is due professors Robert J. Buehler, B. V. Shah, and Oscar Kemphorne of Iowa State University, who let us see their material on the method of parallel tangents before its publication. Industrial colleagues have also made worthy contributions: S. M. Johnson of the RAND Corporation, Robert Hooke, T. A. Jeeves, and Cy Wood of Westinghouse, Ed Blum of Pure Oil, Shahen Hovanessian and the group at T-R-W Computers, and our old friend Gene Motte of Union Oil.

We must also thank the colleagues who brought important material to our attention which might otherwise have been overlooked: Leroy Folks of Oklahoma State, Jim Carley of The University of Arizona, David Himmelblau of The University of Texas, Dale Rudd of The University of Wisconsin, and Alvin Harkins of the Monsanto Chemical Company. A citation for courage should be awarded Professors Robert Adler and Earl Gose of the Case Institute of Technology, who were the first to use this book for part of a course on optimization theory. The author is also indebted to the institutions which supported him both morally and financially during the conception, classroom presentation, and writing of the book. They are, in order of appearance, The U.S. Education Commission in France, who supported a Fulbright lectureship at the Ecole Nationale Supérieure des Industries Chimiques in Nancy, France; the Israel Institute of Technology (Technion) in Haifa, Israel; The University of Texas, Austin; the National Science Foundation, who invited the author to present this material at the 1962 Process Dynamics and Optimization summer course for Engineering Professors held at the University of Colorado in Boulder; and Yale University. To the shade of the poet Henry Wadsworth Longfellow, who in his poem "Excelsior" also considered the problem of attaining the heights, the author offers his humble respects.

DOUGLASS J. WILDE

Contents

3. The Geometry of Multidimensional Response Surfaces 53

4. Tangents and Gradients 92

5. Acceleration Along a Ridge 123

6. Experimental Error   159

Index   195

Optimum
Seeking
Methods

Search Problems

1

The shades of night were falling fast,
As through an Alpine village passed
A youth, who bore, 'mid snow and ice,
A banner with the strange device,
Excelsior!
—Longfellow

A scientist confronted by a system more or less unknown to him gains knowledge about it by making experiments. He fixes the variables under his control at settings of his choice, notes down the values of any factors he is unable to regulate, and then observes the results. In general, of course, there may be additional variables influencing the outcome which can be neither measured nor controlled; these are the factors behind the *experimental error*. Scientists are not the only people concerned with studying unknown systems, as Table 1-1 illustrates.

Although an experimental approach has always characterized the empirical sciences and may date all the way back to Eve's historic investigation of the apple in the Garden of Eden, there recently has been a renewal of interest in the basic nature of such investigations, often called "black-box" problems for reasons shown in the last line of Table 1-1. The next to last line, dealing with the mathematician's study of functions, gives the nomenclature and notation we shall use in discussing this problem.

In this book we are not particularly interested in finding out all there is to know about the system. We merely wish to determine what settings of the independent variables will yield the optimal (maximum or minimum, whichever is desired) value of whatever dependent variable is taken as a criterion of effectiveness. Let us then consider optimization problems in which the functional dependence of the efficiency criterion upon the adjustable variables is not known. Assume further that the total number n of experiments we can perform is limited. Any set of instructions for

Table 1-1

INVESTIGATION OF UNKNOWN SYSTEMS

Investigator	System	Adjustable Factors	Uncontrollable but Measurable Factors	Unknown Factors	Results
Farmer	Farmland	Fertilizer	Weather	Soil condition	Crop quality
Physician	Patient	Medicine	Pulse rate	Infection	Blood count
Engineer	Chemical reactor	Temperatures	Raw material composition	Activity of catalyst	Product yield
Detective	Suspect	Interrogation	Material evidence	Character of suspect	Testimony
Senator	Senate	Speech	Current events	Personalities of colleagues	Votes on bill
Sales manager	Market	Price of product	Competitors' prices	Public taste	Sales
Mathematician	Function $f(x, p, r)$	Independent variables x	Parameters p	Random variables r	Dependent variable $y=f(x,p,r)$
Anybody	"Black box"	Input knobs	Gauges	State of box	Output readings

placing the n experiments $x_1, x_2, \ldots, x_n$ will be called a *search plan,* and any investigation seeking the optimal value of an unknown function will be called a *search problem.* We want of course to find, from among all possible search plans, the one which looks for this optimum in an optimal manner. Thus we are not only trying to optimize the *function*; we are also optimizing the *optimization procedure.*

Search problems occur for several reasons. The theory describing a real system is rarely perfect, and many approximations are made during conception, design, and construction. Moreover, important parameters may change as time passes. And even with perfect theory and invariant parameters, errors of measurement often obscure the true relationship between output and input. While scientific theory is useful for finding nearly optimal conditions, the preliminary estimate often can be improved by experimenting directly with the system itself, be it a set of equations, a steel mill, or a truck farm.

1.01. Types of search problem

Search problems can be classified according to their number of independent variables and to whether or not experimental error is present. Except for the last chapter on stochastic approximation, we will deal with the error-free or deterministic case. When there is but one independent variable and no random error, elegant and powerful methods for finding an optimum are available; these will be described in Chap. 2. Unfortunately such procedures cannot be extended to problems with more than one independent variable, and many different techniques have been developed for handling the multivariable case. These will be described for the most part in Chaps. 4 and 5 after an introduction to multidimensional geometry in Chap. 3. The presence of experimental error slows down a search considerably and nullifies the essential advantage that univariable problems had over multivariable ones in the deterministic case. Thus in Chap. 6 all types of error-ridden situation are treated alike, regardless of the number of variables.

1.02. Roots and peaks

The problem of locating a peak is very much like that of finding a root. Many root-finding situations, where computationally convenient, have been formulated as minimization problems. Consider, for example, m simultaneous equations

$$\varphi_j(x_1, \ldots, x_k) = 0 \qquad (j = 1, 2, \ldots, m)$$

in the k unknowns x_1 through x_k. One can find solutions to this system of equations by minimizing the function Φ obtained by adding the squares of the left members φ_j. More properly, since the solutions may be complex, the function to be minimized should be

$$\Phi \equiv \sum_{j=1}^{k} \varphi_j \bar{\varphi}_j$$

where $\bar{\varphi}_j$ is the complex conjugate of φ_j. If $k = m$, then at the solution Φ will be at its minimum value zero. But if there are more equations than variables, as is usually the case in curve fitting problems, the minimum value of Φ may not be zero. Such a "solution" would represent a least-squares approximation.[†]

Just as root problems can be transformed into exercises in minimization, optimization problems can be solved by root-finding techniques. This is because the first derivatives of a continuous function must vanish at an extreme point. Hence by working with derivatives of the function to be optimized one can sometimes use well-known root-finding procedures to locate the optimum. The reader should keep in mind that the methods developed in this book, while specially suited to optimization problems, could perhaps be adapted to root location as well.

[†] A. D. Booth, "An Application of the Method of Steepest Descents to the Solution of Systems of Nonlinear Simultaneous Equations," *Quart. J. Mech. Appl. Math.*, **2**, 4 (1949), p. 460.

1.03. Deterministic problems

Search problems having no unknown or random factors will be described as *deterministic.* Assuming that the investigator can correct for any uncontrollable but known factors affecting the system under study, we lose no generality in treating a simplified system having only adjustable variables on which depends some criterion y to be optimized.

In many systems the experimental error cannot be neglected. Yet there are interesting practical optimization problems that are wholly deterministic, as when the criterion of effectiveness is too involved to be optimized directly by such standard techniques as the differential calculus. Economic studies and engineering design problems for example, must usually be considered search problems because of the complexity of the mathematical model used—the equations, tables, graphs, or computer codes. When, as is often the case, the model involves no random elements, the search problem is entirely deterministic, even if the key figures are only approximations based on shaky assumptions, rules of thumb, and imperfect data. It would of course be unwise to expend very much searching effort on a model of questionable accuracy. But this does not affect our problem here, which is how to conduct the search effectively.

1.04. Stochastic problems

If experimental error cannot be neglected, the problem will be called *stochastic,* a word meaning that random factors are involved. Stochastic problems are naturally more difficult than deterministic ones, although not as hard as one might think at first. We shall see that it is possible to consider a stochastic problem as a deterministic one with noise, or experimental error, superimposed. In this way the problem of convergence of the deterministic part can be treated separately from that of the nullification of the noise.

The main effect of random error is to slow down the speed at which a search can be conducted and still be sure of eventually finding the optimum. Stochastic procedures, being very deliberate, should not be used in the absence of experimental error, for deterministic methods are much faster. This point has not been well understood in the past, and stochastic procedures have sometimes been applied to deterministic problems with disappointing results. One can avoid misapplication by remembering that stochastic methods must face a convergence problem that simply does not arise when there is never any danger of a mistake. Thus *speed* of convergence, which is the only consideration in deterministic problems, is only of secondary importance when there is noise.

1.05. Simultaneous and sequential procedures

Search plans fall naturally into two mutually exclusive classes which we shall call *simultaneous* and *sequential*. Plans specifying the location of every experiment before any results are known will be called *simultaneous,* while a plan permitting the experimenter to base future experiments on past outcomes will be called *sequential.*

Suppose, for illustration, that ten economists were available to analyze a capital investment program. Let us say that each economist, if given a tentative distribution of the capital, can, after about a week of calculation, estimate the return on the investment. If the group has only a week to prepare a recommendation, then a ten experiment simultaneous search plan is needed to pick the cases to be studied, for no one has the time to wait for the results of one case before choosing the conditions for another.

When this can be done, it is much more effective to use a *sequential* search plan. If the ten economists could team up and together analyze a case in half a day (assuming a five day week for economists), they could locate the optimum as effectively after analyzing only four cases sequentially as they could by analyzing ten simultaneously. And if instead of going home on Tuesday they continued analyzing cases all week, their ten sequential cases would be almost eighteen times as effective in locating the optimum as would the ten simultaneous cases—provided the sequential search plan were the optimal one. We shall see that the advantage of sequential plans over simultaneous plans increases exponentially with the number of experiments. The branch of statistics known as *experimental design* is usually concerned more with simultaneous than with sequential procedures, and since many good texts on this subject are available, we shall not spend very much time on it.

1.06. Exploitation of partial knowledge

When absolutely nothing can be assumed in advance about the behavior of the system, all an investigator can do is take random measurements and hope for the best. Fortunately, natural systems rarely behave so mysteriously, and usually a few things can be assumed before making any experiments. Thus the criterion of effectiveness is often a continuous function of the independent variables; many times it can be assumed to have but one peak in the region of interest. This book shows how to exploit such partial knowledge to develop efficient search techniques. In order to do this we shall have to perform a bit of what the mathematicians call *analysis* of functions. This means characterizing, in precise, quantitative terms, such intuitive concepts as unimodality (single-peakedness), smoothness, convexity, and similarity. We shall also need to describe—and extend to many dimensions—such geometric or even geographic ideas as peak, valley, ridge, pass or saddle, curvature, and slope. Like any good explorer, we can find our goal sooner if we know something of the lay of the land.

1.07. Multimodality, constraint, and time

After scanning the table of contents the reader will perhaps notice that several interesting topics related to experimental optimization are not discussed. For example there is no attempt to tackle multimodal problems having more than one peak because such situations have not been studied with any success so far. Anyone confronted with such a problem must at present try to isolate the various peaks and explore each of them individually. Hopefully, methods for handling multimodality will be available soon.

Likewise, there is no discussion of constrained optimization problems, in which certain combinations of variables are forbidden which would otherwise be optimal. In spite of its importance, this topic was omitted because there are already many books and articles discussing it. Readers interested in constrained optimization problems would do well to examine the literature on *linear programming, nonlinear* or *mathematical programming,* and *dynamic programming,* some of which is listed in the bibliography at the end of this chapter.

We will confine ourselves here to static problems, those in which the system does not change as time passes. A great deal of research on the dynamic case, where changes do take place, is now under way; some of this is listed in the bibliography. Dynamic problems, often involving *adaptive control,* have not been discussed here because, although much progress has been made on them, there is still much to be done. Moreover, the theoretical background needed, being still too strong for engineering seniors, would be inappropriate here.

1.08. Representation and scaling

Before beginning a search one should devote a little time to the choice of a good representation of the function and to the choice of scales of measurement. We are paraphrasing here the very sensible remarks on these matters expressed by Buehler, Shah, and Kempthorne.[†] They distinguish between the *relationship* between variables and the various *representations* of the relationship. For example, if we are investigating the dependence of chemical process yield on the adjustable operating variables, pressure and temperature, and if y is yield in grams, p is pressure in

[†] R. J. Buehler, B. V. Shah, and O. Kempthorne, "Some Properties of Steepest Ascent and Related Procedures for Finding Optimum Conditions," Iowa State University Statistical Laboratory (April 1961), pp. 8–10, 18.

atmospheres, π is the natural logarithm of p, and t is absolute temperature in degrees Kelvin, then the following expressions are two different *representations* of the same *relationship*.

$$y = \varphi(p, t) = y_0[1 - a(p - p_0)^2 - b(t - t_0)^2] \qquad (1\text{-}1a)$$
$$y = \psi(\pi, t) = y_0[1 - a(e^\pi - p_0)^2 - b(t - t_0)^2] \qquad (1\text{-}1b)$$

A good rule to follow is to choose a representation that can be approximated readily, at least in the neighborhood of the optimum, by a fairly low degree Taylor expansion. This is because most search techniques involve constructing approximations from measured estimates of first and second derivatives. By this rule, the quadratic representation Eq. (1-1a) is preferable to the other one involving the transcendental e^π term.

Another good rule is to prefer representations in which the factors do not interact. This criterion is satisfied by both Eqs. (1-1), since there is no term involving products of the two factors. However, the following representation, in which

$$x_1 = \tfrac{1}{2}(p - p_0) + \tfrac{1}{2}(t - t_0)$$

and

$$x_2 = \tfrac{1}{2}(p - p_0) - \tfrac{1}{2}(t - t_0)$$

shows interaction between x_1 and x_2 because of the term $x_1 x_2$.

$$y = \theta(x_1, x_2) = y_0[1 - (a + b)(x_1^2 + x_2^2) - 2(a - b)x_1 x_2] \qquad (1\text{-}2)$$

Methods for removing interaction are described in Secs. 3.16 and 5.16.

Finally it is good to select scales of measurement in which a unit change in one factor *at the optimum* gives the same change in the dependent variable as a unit change in any other factor. Thus if representation of Eq. (1-1a) were used we would want the scales of p and t to be such that

$$a(p - p_0)^2 = b(t - t_0)^2 \qquad (1\text{-}3)$$

This scaling rule, developed for a particular search procedure described in Sec. 4.13, turns out to be suitable for other procedures as well.

In geometric terms, these rules together tend to make the contours of the dependent variable spherical—symmetrical in all factors. It would of course rarely be the case that enough is known about the function to permit application of the rules. They are intended merely as a guide to educated guesses that tend, if accurate, to speed up the search procedure. Figure 1-1 contrasts a good and a bad choice of scale and representation.

1.09. Plausible reasoning

Before proceeding further, permit us a comment about the manner of presentation. Since we would like to see optimization theory covered in

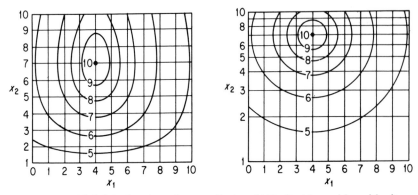

Fig. 1-1. (a) Original rectangular coordinates. (b) Preferable semi-logarithmic coordinates with scale change.

undergraduate engineering or economics curricula, where the students are not always used to formal logic, we have tried to make our definitions precise and our arguments rigorous. But, following the method of G. Polya[†] in his books on plausible reasoning, we have avoided the usual mathematical mode of exposition involving terse statement of formal theorems followed by formal proofs. As one of our purposes is to stimulate the student's creative imagination, we build up the results in the more or less intuitive manner of the original researcher groping toward new concepts. The reader who is more concerned with results than with how they are obtained will do well to skip over some of the details given. But the man who might want to do research in optimization theory—and there's much to be done—may prefer to develop his "feel" for the subject by closely following our plausible, if not always elegant, exposition and by working out formal proofs on his own.

SELECTED BIBLIOGRAPHY ON RELATED SUBJECTS

STEADY STATE CONSTRAINED OPTIMIZATION

Aris, R., *The Optimal Design of Chemical Reactors*. New York: Academic Press, 1961.

Hadley, G., *Linear Programming*. Reading, Mass.: Addison-Wesley Publishing Co., Inc., 1962.

Vajda, S., *Mathematical Programming*. Reading, Mass.: Addison-Wesley Publishing Co., Inc., 1961.

[†] G. Polya, *How to Solve It* (Princeton: Princeton University Press, 1945).

———, *Induction and Analogy in Mathematics* (Princeton: Princeton University Press, 1954).

UNSTEADY STATE CONSTRAINED OPTIMIZATION

Bellman, R., and S. Dreyfus, *Applied Dynamic Programming*. Princeton: Princeton University Press, 1962.

OPTIMAL CONTROL

Bellman, R., *Adaptive Control Processes*: *A Guided Tour*. Princeton: Princeton University Press, 1960.
Chang, S. S. L., *Synthesis of Optimal Control Systems*. New York: McGraw-Hill Book Co., Inc., 1961.

EXPERIMENTAL DESIGN

Davies, O. L. (ed.), *The Design and Analysis of Industrial Experiments*. New York: Hafner Publishing Co., Inc., 1956.

EXERCISES

1. Suggest physical or economic optimization problems which are
   (a) deterministic, single variable.
   (b) deterministic, multivariable.
   (c) stochastic, single variable.
   (d) stochastic, multivariable.

2. Express the finding of the solution to the simultaneous equations

$$x_1 + 5x_2 = 13$$
$$x_1^2 + x_2^2 = 13$$

   as an optimization problem.

3. Suggest a suitable representation and scaling, with changes of variable if necessary, for the preceding optimization problem.

4. Find transformations that will make the variables non-interacting in the following functions.
   (a) $3x_1^2 + 5x_1x_2 - 2x_2^2$
   (b) $x_1^4 e^{-3x_2^2}$
   (c) $(e^{-x_1^2} + 2x_2)(3e^{-2x_2} + x_1)$
   (d) $\exp(-x_1^2 + 5x_1x_2 - 4x_2^2)$

5. Suggest scaling units for x_1 and x_2 in the following cases.
   (a) $\ln(x_1^2 + 3x_2^2)$
   (b) $\cos(x_1^2 + x_1x_2 + 3x_2)^2$

Single Variable Search 2

Consider the simplest case where there is but one adjustable variable x and no experimental error. Optimal policies will be derived for sequential as well as simultaneous search. The results for problems with many independent variables, not being as clear cut, will be deferred to the two chapters following on *multivariable search*.

After defining unimodality and showing how this very general property permits us to choose the objective *minimax* measure of searching effectiveness, we proceed to optimize the measure for both simultaneous and sequential plans. This leads naturally to the interesting and highly effective *Fibonacci* search method which, despite its rather recent discovery by Kiefer, has theoretical connections with problems dating all the way back to Euclid. Eventually we shall encounter the bizarre technique of *randomization,* in which search directions are determined by the flip of a coin.

2.01. Unimodality

We need to describe, in precise mathematical terms, functions y of a single variable x which, roughly speaking, have only one hump in the interval to be explored. All of the functions pictured in Fig. 2-1 have this property, which we shall call *unimodality*. Notice that a unimodal function does not have to be smooth as in Fig. 2-1(a), or even continuous as in Fig. 2-1(b); it can be broken, discontinuous, and even undefined in certain intervals as in Fig. 2-1(c). Thus, the unimodality assumption, not really very restrictive, holds in a large number of practical search problems.

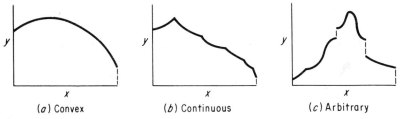

(a) Convex   (b) Continuous   (c) Arbitrary

Fig. 2-1. Unimodal functions.

Let y be a function of an independent variable x' restricted to a closed interval running from $x' = a$ to $x' = b$: $a \le x' \le 0$. No generality is lost, and much simplicity is gained, by working with a transformed variable x which is zero when $x' = a$ and unity when $x' = b$. The new dimensionless variable, defined by $x \equiv (x' - a)/(b - a)$, is simply the fraction of the interval lying to the left of x', and clearly $0 \le x \le 1$.

Suppose, to be more definite, that we wish to *maximize y*. If necessary, a minimization problem always can be changed into this form simply by seeking the greatest value of $(-y)$ rather than the least value of y. Let y^* be the desired but unknown maximum value of y, and let x^* be the value of x for which this maximum is attained. That is, $y^* \equiv \max_x y(x)$ and $y(x^*) \equiv y^*$.

As x moves away from x^*, y will always decrease if it is a unimodal function of x. The engineer, used to dealing with continuous functions and rates of change, might be tempted to define unimodality by using derivatives in the following manner: y is unimodal if $x < x^*$ implies that $dy/dx > 0$, and if $x > x^*$ implies that $dy/dx < 0$. While this definition would be satisfactory for the smooth continuous functions shown in Figs. 2-1(a) and 2-1(b), it could not be applied to the broken and discontinuous function of Fig. 2-1(c). To handle this last case we must define unimodality without using derivatives. This forces us to work with *pairs* of experiments, for a single trial can give no information about the trend of a function.

Consider two experiments x_1 and x_2, with $x_1 < x_2$, and let their outcomes be y_1 and y_2 respectively. Then y is *unimodal* if $x_2 < x^*$ implies that $y_1 < y_2$, and if $x_1 > x^*$ implies that $y_1 > y_2$. In other words, if the points are both on the same side of the optimum, then the one nearer the optimum gives the higher value of y. This definition is strong enough to build a measure of search effectiveness, without being so restrictive as to exclude many practical functions behaving discontinuously. In passing, however, it would be worthwhile to mention some special types of unimodal functions whose definitions are more restrictive.

We have already mentioned the unimodal continuous function shown in Figs. 2-1(a) and 2-1(b). Figure 2-1(a) shows the even more restricted *convex* function which appears often enough in the literature on optimization to warrant mention here. Consider values of y_1, y_2, and y_3 corresponding to any three abscissae x_1, x_2 and x_3, with $x_1 < x_2 < x_3$. The value of y at x_2 could of course be estimated by linear interpolation between y_1 and y_3, the interpolation giving an estimate equal to

$$y_1 \frac{x_3 - x_2}{x_3 - x_1} + y_3 \frac{x_2 - x_1}{x_3 - x_1}$$

When the true value y_2 is always greater than this estimate, we say that the function is *convex*. A single-valued convex function necessarily will be unimodal, although it does not have to be continuous like the curve in Fig. 2-1(a). A convex function cannot have points of inflection, which is why Fig. 2-1(b) is not convex.

Unimodality, when it can be assumed, makes it possible to say, after examining the results of any pair of experiments, that the optimum x^* lies in some interval smaller than the original one. Consider two experiments x_1 and x_2, with $x_1 < x_2$. The possible outcomes can be divided into the three cases shown in Fig. 2-2:

$$y_1 > y_2, \qquad y_1 < y_2, \quad \text{or} \quad y_1 = y_2$$

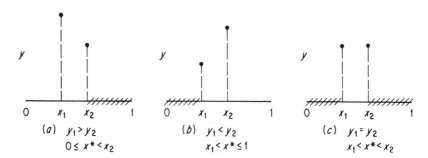

Fig. 2-2. Possible outcomes of two experiments.

Now if $y_1 < y_2$, as in Fig. 2-2(a), then the optimum could not possibly be to the right of x_2 without contradicting the assumption that y is unimodal. For the reader who is not used to proving things by contradiction we shall go through the details of the proof, which are really quite simple, because arguments of this form could be just as useful to practitioners of the applied sciences as they have always been to their more theoretically inclined colleagues. Anyone already understanding this technique of *reductio ad absurdum* (reduction to an absurdity) could profitably omit the next two paragraphs.

We want to show that if y is unimodal and $y_1 > y_2$, then the optimum x^* cannot lie to the right of x_2. To prove this theorem by contradiction, we temporarily assume the contrary, that is, that $x^* > x_2$. By following this assumption to its logical conclusion, we deduce something known to be false, which shows that our temporary assumption must have been false. But since the temporary assumption was contrary to the theorem, the falseness of the former establishes the validity of the latter. The proof itself follows.

Suppose, contrary to the theorem, that $x^* > x_2$. Then both x_1 and x_2 would be on the same side of x^*: $x_1 < x_2 < x^*$. From the definition of unimodality, this would imply that $y_1 < y_2$. This obviously contradicts the hypothesis of the theorem, which states that $y_1 > y_2$. Hence it cannot be true that $x^* > x_2$, and we conclude that $0 < x^* < x_2$.

By similar reasoning it can be proven that if $x_1 < x_2$, then $x_1 < x^* \leq 1$, as shown in Fig. 2-2(b). When considered together, the two cases already analyzed cover the third case, shown in Fig. 2-2(c). Thus when the two responses are equal, the optimum must lie between the two experiments.

Before using these results to develop an objective measure of effectiveness for search plans, we should comment on the unimodality hypothesis itself, since all of the work to follow will depend on it. No one, to our knowledge, has yet made a systematic study of common mathematical models to see which criteria are really unimodal. However, we can cite a few important optimization problems having unimodal measures of effectiveness. The equilibrium composition of a mixture of reacting chemical compounds is known from thermodynamic principles to be that at which a certain function called the *free energy* is minimum. Selmer Johnson[†] has pointed out that this function is concave up, which as we have already remarked, implies its unimodality. In economics, the well-known "Law of Diminishing Returns" gives a profit function which is concave down with respect to the amount invested. In our own experience, we have never seen an optimization problem where, in the range of investigation, the criterion of effectiveness was not unimodal. Considering our present ignorance of the subject, we can only recommend enough preliminary investigation—theoretical or experimental—of any search problem to guarantee that the interval of search encompasses the highest summit and no other.

MEASURING SEARCH EFFECTIVENESS

Before we can talk about an *optimal* search plan, we must have an *a priori* criterion of searching effectiveness. By this we mean a measure that

[†] Johnson, S. M., *Management Science*, **5** (1959), p. 299.

can be evaluated from examining the search plan alone, *before* any experiments have actually been carried out. Thus, although it would be tempting to measure a search's effectiveness by the highest value of the dependent variable attained experimentally, such a criterion would depend on luck as well as planning skill, hardly an acceptable state of affairs. Fortunately, when the function to be explored is unimodal an a priori criterion, depending on the placement of the experiments but not at all on their outcomes, can be defined precisely and then optimized.

Let us study a particular search plan, develop an a priori criterion of effectiveness for it, and then generalize the criterion. Suppose, to be definite, that three experiments are to be run at locations respectively ten, forty, and eighty percent of the distance from the left end of the original interval of uncertainty. Numbering the experiments from left to right, we have $x_1 = 0.1$, $x_2 = 0.4$, and $x_3 = 0.8$, as shown in Fig. 2-3. Let K be the index of the experiment x_K producing the greatest outcome y_K. That is, K is such that

$$y_K \equiv \max_{1 \leq k \leq n} \{y_k\} \quad \text{and} \quad y(x_K) \equiv y_K$$

Notice that y_K, the maximum obtained by the particular series of experiments, is not necessarily equal to y^*, the maximum attainable.

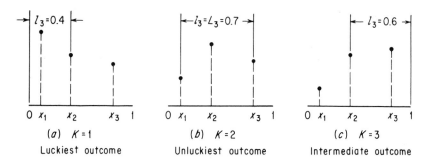

Fig. 2-3. An undistinguished search plan:

$$x_1 = 0.1, \quad x_2 = 0.4, \quad x_3 = 0.8$$

As shown in Fig. 2-3, the possible outcomes fall into three groups according to whether the maximum is obtained by the first, second, or third experiment. In each case we can, using the results of the preceding section, narrow down the interval in which we know the optimum x^* to lie. Thus, if $K = 1$, then $0 \leq x^* \leq x_2$; if $K = 2$, then $x_1 \leq x^* \leq x_3$; and if $K = 3$, then $x_2 \leq x^* \leq 1$.

2.02. Interval of uncertainty

To express these facts more compactly, and in a form which can be generalized to cover a search involving n experiments, let us denote the left and right ends of the original interval by x_0 and x_{n+1} respectively; that is, $x_0 \equiv 0$ and $x_{n+1} \equiv 1$. Then for a set of n experiments, we can say in general that $x_{K-1} \leq x^* \leq x_{K+1}$. We shall call this region the *interval of uncertainty after n experiments* and denote its length by l_n.

$$l_n \equiv x_{K+1} - x_{K-1} \tag{2-1}$$

Thus the final interval of uncertainty lies between the experiments on either side of the one producing the highest value of y. In Fig. 2-3, l_3 takes on the values 0.4, 0.7, or 0.6, depending on whether the maximum for the three experiments is attained on the first, second, or third trial.

In general a search plan specifies the size of the possible final intervals $x_{k+1} - x_{k-1}$ ($k = 1, 2, \ldots, n$), while the experimental results y_k determine K, the index of both the experiment with the best outcome and the final interval of uncertainty l_n. To show this simultaneous dependence of l_n on the planned x_k and the experimental results determining K, let us write the length of the final interval in functional notation as $l_n(x_k, K)$.

After a series of experiments has been carried out and the results measured, l_n will be a good indication of how effective the search has been. But since we cannot predict l_n before running the experiments, l_n does not satisfy our requirements for an a priori measure of effectiveness.

Let us concern ourselves then not with all of the n intervals possible, but only with the longest, designated L_n. Then no matter how the experimental results actually turn out, we can always be sure that the final interval of uncertainty will be no greater than L_n. And if we are lucky, we may be able to do better.

From the very definition of the maximum length L_n we see that it depends only on the search plan, not on which interval happens to contain the optimum point x^*.

$$L_n(x_k) \equiv \max_{1 \leq K \leq n} \{l_n(x_k, K)\}$$

In our three experiment example, the maximum length of L_3 is given by

$$L_3(0.1, 0.4, 0.8) = \max_{1 \leq K \leq 3} \{l_n(x_k, 1), l_n(x_k, 2), l_n(x_k, 3)\}$$
$$= \max \{(x_2 - x_0), (x_3 - x_1), (x_4 - x_2)\}$$
$$= \max \{0.4, 0.7, 0.6\}$$
$$= 0.7$$

L_n is unique, for although there are many possible final lengths l_n, there is only one *longest* length. Because L_n is deliberately chosen to correspond to the worst possible outcome, it is completely free of trouble-some dependence on experimental results. Instead of trying to guess *which* interval of uncertainty will remain, we simply deal with the longest that might turn up if our luck is bad. Thus by confining our attention to an extreme case, we actually simplify the problem, obtaining an a priori, if pessimistic, measure of search effectiveness.

2.03. The minimax concept

We now seek from among all possible search plans the one making L_n, our newly defined measure of effectiveness, as small as possible. Denoting the experiments in the optimal plan by x_k^* and the interval of uncertainty for this plan by L_n^*, we have

$$L_n^* \equiv \min_{x_k} \{L_n(x_k)\} \quad \text{and} \quad L_n(x_k^*) \equiv L_n^* \tag{2-2}$$

Although L_n is a variable which depends on what search plan is used, L_n^* is a constant. Again we see that optimization has simplified our prob-lem, for the act of minimization has narrowed down the wide range of possible final intervals of uncertainty to a single one, the smallest. Although L_n^* is unique, there may be more than one search plan x_k^* giving this final interval, as we shall see in our study of simultaneous search.

The plan x_k^* is often called a *minimax* scheme, for by combining Eqs. (2-1) and (2-2) we may write L_n^* as

$$L_n^* \equiv \min_{x_k} \max_{1 \leq K \leq n} \{l_n(x_k, K)\}$$

The two optimizations have in fact selected a single value L_n^* from among all the intervals l_n which could arise from diverse search plans and various outcomes. Notice that the order of these operations is very important, any other combination giving completely trivial results. Two maximizations would give the *worst* possible search plan.

$$\max_{x_k} \max_{1 \leq K \leq n} \{l_n(x_k, K)\} = 1$$

And since dealing with the shortest possible interval l_n would be to con-sider only the *luckiest* results, minimizing l_n would only lead to complete degeneracy.

$$\min_{1 \leq k \leq n} \{l_n(x_k, K)\} = 0$$

Only the minimax approach gives a meaningful, non-trivial search plan.

A minimax plan is completely conservative, chance determining only the position of its final interval, not the length. Yet in spite of its rather pessimistic and cautious basis, the minimax concept leads to surprisingly effective search methods.

The minimax concept has wide application to decision problems, even those involving two competitors. The following slightly modified passage from *The Compleat Strategyst,* the amusing and instructive "primer" on games of strategy by J. D. Williams (New York: McGraw-Hill Book Co., Inc., 1954), illustrates the minimax concept as applied to the theory of games. Optimal strategy and the theory of games will be discussed more extensively at the end of the chapter.

> Let's suppose that a man and wife—being very specific always helps, so let's name them Ray and Dotty—are planning a camping trip, and that Ray likes high altitudes and Dotty likes low altitudes. The region of interest to them is crisscrossed by a network of fire divides, or roads, four running in each direction. The campers have agreed to camp at a road junction. They have further agreed that Ray will choose the east-west road and that Dotty will choose the north-south road, which jointly identify the junction. If Game Theory doesn't save them, frustration will kill them.
>
> The junctions on the roads available to Ray have these altitudes (in thousands of feet):

	Road	Altitude			
	1	7	2	5	1
Ray	2	2	2	3	4
	3	5	3	4	4
	4	3	2	1	6

Being a reasonable person, who simply wants to make as much as possible out of this affair, he is naturally attracted to the road Ray 1—with junctions at altitudes of 7, 2, 5, and 1—for it alone can get him the 7-thousand-foot peak. However, he immediately recognizes this kind of thinking as dream stuff; he does not dare undertake a plan which would realize him a great deal if it succeeds, but which would lead to disaster if Dotty is skillful in her choice. Not anticipating that she will choose carelessly, his own interests compel him to ignore the breath-taking peaks; instead, he must attend particularly to the sinks and lows of one kind and another, which blemish the region. This study leads him finally to the road Ray 3, which has as attractive a low as the region affords, namely, one at an altitude of 3 thousand feet. By choosing Ray 3, he can ensure that the camp site will be at least 3 thousand feet up; it will be higher, if Dotty is a little careless.

His wife—as he feared—is just as bright about these matters as he is. The critical altitudes on her roads are listed in the following table:

	Dotty			
Road	1	2	3	4
	7	2	5	1
Altitude	2	2	3	4
	5	3	4	4
	3	2	1	6

As she examines these, she knows better than to waste time mooning over the deep valleys of Dotty 3 and Dotty 4, much as she would like to camp there. Being a realist, she examines the peaks which occur on her roads, determined to choose a road which contains only little ones. She is thus led, finally, to Dotty 2, where a 3-thousand-foot camp site is the worst that can be inflicted on her.

We now note that something in the nature of a coincidence has occurred. Ray has a strategy (Ray 3) which guarantees that the camp site will have an altitude of 3 thousand feet or more, and Dotty has one (Dotty 2) which ensures that it will be 3 thousand feet or less. In other words, either player can get a 3-thousand-foot camp site by his own efforts, in the face of a skillful opponent; and he will do somewhat better than this if his opponent is careless.

Note too that security measures are not strictly necessary. Either Ray or Dotty can openly announce a choice (if it is the proper one), and the other will be unable to exploit the information and force the other beyond the 3-thousand-foot site.

Both competitors in this example are using a minimax strategy. Dotty minimizes the maximum elevation of the camp site, while Ray minimizes the maximum *difference* in elevation between the camp and the highest peak. In this special case, the two simple minimax strategies coincide and Dotty and Ray camp at a pass or *saddlepoint,* which does not always happen. But we shall see at the end of the chapter that the minimax concept can be extended to cover more general competitive situations. For the moment, all we need to know is that the minimax approach does yield definite answers to our search problem.

SIMULTANEOUS SEARCH

When all experiments must be run at the same time, it is necessary to use a simultaneous search plan. Naturally, simultaneous schemes are much less effective than sequential plans, in which one may base the locations of later experiments on the results of earlier ones. But there are situations where the experimenter is forced to use a simultaneous plan, inefficient as it is.

Sometimes one is working against a deadline and cannot spare the time required to run a sequence of trials one after another. Such was the predicament of the ten hypothetical economists of page 5 who could not assign more than one man at a time to analyze any single investment case. Occasionally the investigator's hands are tied by institutional rules requiring the submission of a detailed experimental plan before research funds can be allocated or permission granted to conduct the tests. And often it is necessary to search for an extremum with measuring instruments built right into a piece of equipment, as when one monitors the location of the highest temperature in a tubular chemical reactor studded with thermocouples, or the region of maximum stress along a moving shaft equipped with strain gauges.

2.04. Two experiments

To narrow down the interval of uncertainty one must perform at least two experiments. And since information from the first experiment is of no help in placing the second, a simultaneous plan is just as good as a sequential one when only two experiments can be used. Therefore let us begin our discussion of search plans by studying this simplest possible case: $n = 2$.

Consider then two experiments, one at x_1 and the other at x_2, with $0 \leq x_1 < x_2 \leq 1$. Applying Eqs. (2-1) and (2-2) we may write the maximum interval of uncertainty L_2 as a function of x_1 and x_2.

$$L_2 \equiv \max \{(x_2 - x_0), (x_3 - x_1)\} = \max \{x_2, 1 - x_1\}$$

Contours of this function, whose nature may be somewhat unfamiliar to the reader, are shown in Fig. 2-4. Only points (x_1, x_2) in the triangular region bounded by $x_1 = 0$, $x_2 = 1$, and $x_1 = x_2$ can be considered because x_1 was defined to be less than x_2. At first glance the minimum value of L_2 in this region may appear to be 0.50, attained where $x_1 = x_2 = \frac{1}{2}$. But of course this possibility is ruled out by the requirement that x_2 be *greater* than x_1.

Let ϵ (epsilon) represent the least separation between two experiments for which a difference between y_1 and y_2 can be detected. Then by placing x_1 at $\frac{1}{2} - (\epsilon/2)$ and x_2 at $\frac{1}{2} + (\epsilon/2)$ we obtain not only the required separation, but also L_2^*, the minimum possible value of L_2. All these facts may be expressed as

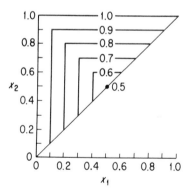

Fig. 2-4. L_2 as a function of x_1 and x_2.

$$L_2^* = L_2 \left[\left(\frac{1}{2} + \frac{\epsilon}{2} \right), \left(\frac{1}{2} + \frac{\epsilon}{2} \right) \right] = \frac{1}{2} + \frac{\epsilon}{2}$$

Whenever it is necessary to take account of ϵ, the minimum permissible separation between experiments, the search scheme is said to be "ϵ-minimax."

2.05. Three experiments

Having found the best arrangement for two experiments, let us now study the three experiment case by trying to improve the rather uninspiring plan of Fig. 2-3, in which $x_1 = 0.1$, $x_2 = 0.4$, $x_3 = 0.8$, and L_3, the greatest possible interval of uncertainty, is 0.7.

Figure 2-3(b) shows that L_3 can be decreased by moving x_1 and x_3 toward each other, so let us increase x_1 to 0.2 and decrease x_3 to 0.7 as in Fig. 2-5. This makes $x_3 - x_1 = 0.5$, but now the longest possible interval is between x_2 and the right end of the interval. However L_3 has been reduced to $x_4 - x_2 = 1 - 0.4 = 0.6$.

L_3 can be diminished further by displacing x_2 to the right, decreasing $x_4 - x_2$. But in doing this we also increase $x_2 - x_0$. To decide where to put x_2 we consider the function

$$\max \{x_2, (1 - x_2)\}$$

in the range $0.2 = x_1 < x_2 < x_3 = 0.7$ (Fig. 2-6).

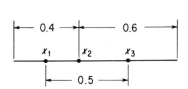

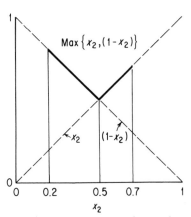

Fig. 2-5. An improved simultaneous search plan:
$x_1 = 0.2, \quad x_2 = 0.4, \quad x_3 = 0.7$
$L_3 = x_4 - x_2 = 0.6$

Fig. 2-6. Placement of second experiment.

This function being minimum for $x_2 = 0.5$, we place the second experiment there.

Now no matter where the optimum point x^* happens to be, the longest interval of uncertainty will always be 0.5 as shown in Fig. 2-7(a). The point x_2 cannot be moved without increasing either $x_2 - x_0$ or $x_4 - x_2$. And although $x_1 - x_3$ can be decreased below 0.5, this would affect neither $x_2 - x_0$ nor $x_4 - x_2$, which would be the largest, and therefore controlling, intervals of uncertainty. Hence 0.5 is the minimum possible value of L_3, which means that the plan $x_1 = 0.2$, $x_2 = 0.5$ and $x_3 = 0.7$ is minimax, with $L_3^* = 0.5$.

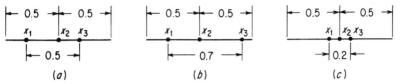

Fig. 2-7. Minimax simultaneous plans for three experiments.

2.06. Uniform pairs

Upon further reflection we see that any simultaneous plan having $x_2 = 0.5$ and $x_3 - x_1 \le 0.5$ is minimax. Two other minimax schemes are shown in Figs. 2-7(b) and 2-7(c). Since $L_2^* - L_3^*$ is only $\epsilon/2$, a third experiment is hardly worth the effort. As a matter of fact, only when the separation ϵ is relatively large would it ever be worthwhile to use an odd number of experiments in a simultaneous search. The best deployment of experiments is in equally spaced pairs as shown in Fig. 2-8. Such an arrangement will be called a *search by uniform pairs*.

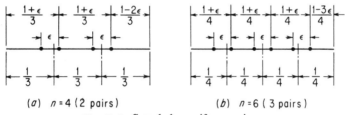

(a) $n = 4$ (2 pairs)   (b) $n = 6$ (3 pairs)

Fig. 2-8. Search by uniform pairs.

In order to write down a formula for placing the experiments in a search by uniform pairs, we must introduce notation that will identify the pair to which a given experiment x_k belongs. Let the placement of square brackets around a variable indicate the greatest integer less than or equal to the variable. For example, $[\frac{x}{2}] = 2$ and $[\pi] = 3$. Then for $k = 1, 2, \ldots, n$ with n even we may write that

$$x_k = \frac{(1 + \epsilon)[(k + 1)/2]}{(n/2) + 1} - \left\{ \left[\frac{k + 1}{2}\right] - \left[\frac{k}{2}\right] \right\} \epsilon \qquad (2\text{-}3)$$

To verify that this scheme is ϵ-minimax for an even number of experiments, one need only observe that displacing any of the experiments from these positions can only increase L_n, the length of the longest interval. The ϵ-minimax length L_n^* is given by

$$L_n^* = \frac{1 + \epsilon}{(n/2) + 1} \qquad (2\text{-}4)$$

To complete the discussion of simultaneous search we shall mention

briefly the optimum placement of an odd number of experiments. Let n
be an *even* number, and consider the following arrangement for $n + 1$
trials. The even-numbered experiments, including the dummy points $x_0 \equiv 0$
and $x_{n+2} \equiv 1$, should be spaced at intervals $2/(n + 2)$. The odd-numbered
experiments may be put anywhere as long as the distance between any
two in succession is no greater than $2/(n + 2)$. Thus when the number
of trials is odd there is an infinity of possible minimax plans, all giving
an interval of uncertainty of length $L^* = 2/(n + 2)$.

Figure 2-9 shows two minimax schemes for five experiments, one with
all trials uniformly spaced and the other with an asymmetric arrangement
of runs 1, 3, and 5. As in the two- and three-experiment cases already
discussed, the improvement in minimax length due to the odd experiment
is only a fraction of the separation factor ϵ, because

$$L_{n+1}^* - L_n^* = \frac{\epsilon}{(n/2) + 1}$$

when n is even.

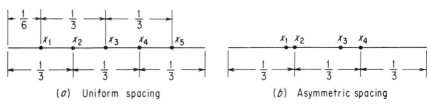

(a) Uniform spacing   (b) Asymmetric spacing

Fig. 2-9. Minimax search plans for five simultaneous experiments.

2.07. Experimental error

In the preceding discussion we had to take account of the fact that no
two experiments could be closer than some positive distance ϵ. The mathematician is not accustomed to worrying about the size of ϵ, and he almost
invariably neglects it entirely. An investigator dealing with a physical or
economic problem cannot always do this however. It behooves us then to
discuss this minimum separation ϵ, especially since in the next section
we shall show how to reduce its effect as much as possible.

A difficulty arises here, for in order to estimate ϵ one must know something about how rapidly the unknown function changes. Unfortunately it
is precisely in the neighborhood of the optimum that the function often
tends to flatten out, for if the function is smooth and continuous its first
derivative will in fact vanish at the optimum unless it is at one end of the
interval. Thus the minimum distance ϵ may be far from negligible.

In our discussion so far we have ignored experimental error for the
sake of simplicity and because we have assumed that the reader has no

statistical background. But even without formal training in statistics the reader can see that experimental error will increase ϵ. One can reduce the effect of experimental error by repeating each experiment and using the average of several measurements, but this of course requires more trials. All that is really required however is a means of knowing whether the difference observed between two outcomes is due to a real difference or merely to a chance fluctuation caused by experimental error. Such *significance tests* are beyond the scope of this work, but they are quite simple and can be found in any standard text on statistics dealing with hypothesis testing.† Our purpose here is merely to warn the reader against employing the proposed methods in the face of large experimental error without controlling them with statistical tests. Search procedures especially designed for combatting experimental error are described in Chap. 6.

SEQUENTIAL SEARCH

A sequential search scheme allows the investigator to run his experiments one after the other, using information from earlier experiments to decide where to locate later ones. This flexibility pays off heavily, even more than one might imagine. And often one can avoid an inefficient simultaneous search simply by changing one's point of view.

As suggested on page 5, if the ten individualistic economists could team up, all working on the same case in order to get the answer sooner, they could study their cases sequentially and, expending no more time than would be needed for a simultaneous search, pinpoint the optimum to within an interval only an eighteenth of that obtainable with a search by uniform pairs. Institutional rules inhibiting a "wait-and-see" approach to a search problem can be changed (sometimes). And with a little foresight one can at times design the instrumentation of a machine to permit sequential measurements, as by having a single movable thermocouple to follow a chemical reactor's high temperature "hot spot" instead of several thermocouples in fixed positions.

2.08. Dichotomous search

In the previous section we showed that when there are only two experiments the best thing to do is place both experiments at the center of the interval, as close together as possible. This leaves an interval of uncertainty of length $[\frac{1}{2} + (\epsilon/2)]$. Suppose we place the third and fourth

† Alexander Mood, *Introduction to the Theory of Statistics* (New York: McGraw-Hill Book Co., Inc., 1950), p. 263.

experiments in the middle of the remaining interval as shown in Fig. 2-10(b). Then the interval of uncertainty would be given by

$$\frac{1}{2}\left(\frac{1}{2}+\frac{\epsilon}{2}\right)+\frac{\epsilon}{2}=\frac{1}{4}+\frac{3\epsilon}{4}$$

After a fifth and sixth experiment, placed in similar fashion, the interval would be down to $\frac{1}{8}+(7\epsilon/8)$, as shown in Fig. 2-10(c). It general, after n experiments (n must be even of course) one can locate the optimum within an interval at length $2^{-n/2}+(1-2^{-n/2})\epsilon$.

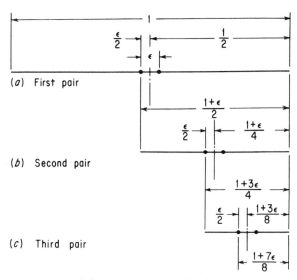

Fig. 2-10. Dichotomous search with six experiments.

Thus the effectiveness of this *dichotomous search* plan, which resembles Bolzano's method for finding a root,[†] grows exponentially with n, while that of a search by uniform pairs increases only in direct proportion to the number of experiments. The price of inflexibility becomes clear when one considers that to reduce an interval of uncertainty to one percent of its original length would, neglecting ϵ, require 198 simultaneous experiments—a task that could be accomplished after only 14 dichotomous trials (see Table 2-1 and Fig. 2-12).

2.09. Fibonacci search

Powerful as the dichotomous technique is, there exists a method that is even better. The ϵ-minimax sequential search scheme was found by

[†] R. G. Stanton, *Numerical Methods for Science and Engineering* (Englewood Cliffs, N. J.: Prentice-Hall, Inc., 1961), pp. 83–84.

Kiefer[†] in 1953. Although this discovery is relatively recent, it has very interesting theoretical connections not only to the work of Fibonacci, a thirteenth century mathematician whose name has been given to the technique, but even to a construction of the ancient geometer Euclid. We shall discuss the historical background of this *Fibonacci search method* shortly, but first we want to derive it and show how it works.

Kiefer, following long-established mathematical tradition, states the method and then proceeds to prove it ϵ-minimax. We prefer here to sacrifice elegance for plausibility, showing how one might go about finding the method in the first place. Our demonstration takes as a model a dynamic programming type proof of Johnson's.[‡] In addition, we incorporate into our demonstration a suggestion of L. Oliver, one of our students, for taking account of the minimum separation ϵ throughout the search, thus obtaining a final interval of uncertainty slightly smaller than Kiefer's, who does not bother with ϵ until it is time to place the very last experiment. Although this economy is only about two-thirds of the separation ϵ, it may sometimes be worth having in practical problems.

Suppose we have n experiments with which to explore sequentially an interval of uncertainty originally of unit length. Consider the situation after all but one of the n experiments have been run. An interval of uncertainty, whose length we shall designate L^*_{n-1}, remains to be searched. As shown in Fig. 2-11(c), somewhere inside this interval will be the experiment E^+_{n-1} which gave the highest outcome y of any of the first $n - 1$ trials. Since the relative location of E^+_{n-1} in the interval L^*_{n-1} depends entirely on what search plan we have used, the position of E^+_{n-1} is in principle completely under our control. And we are of course free to put the last experiment E_n anywhere, as long as it is no closer to E^+_{n-1} than the minimum separation ϵ. Hence no matter what the length L^*_{n-1} happens to be, we can arrange to have E^+_{n-1} and E_n in the locations which will make L^*_n, the length of the final interval, as small as possible. This situation being entirely equivalent to an ordinary search with only two experiments, we already know that these optimal locations are symmetric about the mid-point of L^*_{n-1}, a distance ϵ apart. Thus L^*_{n-1} and L^*_n are related by

$$L^*_{n-1} = 2L^*_n - \epsilon \tag{2-5}$$

as shown in Fig. 2-11(d).

Next consider the interval remaining after all but two of the experiments have been run. Its length will be denoted L^*_{n-2}. Somewhere inside

[†] J. Kiefer, "Sequential Minimax Search for a Maximum," *Proc. Am. Math. Soc.* **4** (1953), p. 502.

[‡] S. M. Johnson, "Optimal Search for a Maximum is Fibonaccian," RAND Corp. report P-856 (1956).

this interval will be the experiment E_{n-2}^{+} yielding the highest outcome of all the first $n-2$ trials. The next experiment, temporarily designated E_{n-1}, is to be conducted somewhere in this interval. After it has been run we will know which of the two points gives the better outcome, and we will change the name of the better point to E_{n-1}^{+}. The other point, which we shall call E_{n-1}^{-}, is the boundary between the portion of L_{n-2}^{*} eliminated and the remaining segment L_{n-1}^{*} to be explored further. Hence the point E_{n-1}^{-} has to be exactly L_{n-1}^{*} units from one end of the interval L_{n-2}^{*}. But when we are planning the experiments, we do not know which of the two points E_{n-2}^{+} and E_{n-1} eventually will turn out to be E_{n-1}^{-}. It follows that *both* E_{n-2}^{+} and E_{n-1} must be a distance L_{n-1}^{*} from the ends of L_{n-2}^{*}, although not of course from the same end.

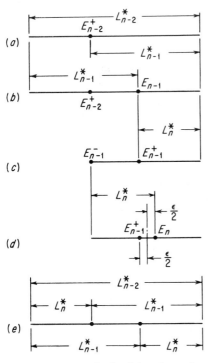

Fig. 2-11. Optimal locations of last two experiments.

An optimal search plan must therefore arrange to have E_{n-2}^{+} exactly L_{n-1}^{*} units from one end of the interval L_{n-2}^{*} (Fig. 2-11(a)). We then place the next experiment E_{n-1} a distance L_{n-1}^{*} from the other end (Fig. 2-11(b)). These two points divide the interval L_{n-2}^{*} into three segments, and the outcomes of the trials determine which of the two end sections will be eliminated from further consideration.

Either E_{n-2}^{+} or E_{n-1} will be in the remaining interval, whose length is L_{n-1}^{*}. The surviving experiment will be in fact what we have called E_{n-1}^{+}, since it is the one with the best outcome among all the first $n-1$ trials. We have already proven that E_{n-1}^{+} must be exactly L_{n}^{*} units away from the end of the interval L_{n-1}^{*} (Fig. 2-11(c)). Since E_{n-2}^{+} and E_{n-2}^{-} were placed symmetrically in the interval L_{n-2}^{*}, and since one of these points will turn out to be E_{n-1}^{-}, it follows that each point must be L_{n}^{*} units from one end of L_{n-2}^{*} and L_{n-1}^{*} units from the other, as shown in Fig. 2-11(e). From this we conclude that

$$L_{n-2}^{*} = L_{n-1}^{*} + L_{n}^{*} \qquad (2\text{-}6)$$

Combining Eqs. (2-5) and (2-6) we obtain

$$L_{n-2}^* = (2L_n^* - \epsilon) + L_n^* = 3L_n^* - \epsilon \qquad (2\text{-}7)$$

This line of reasoning can be generalized quite easily to relate the lengths of any three successive intervals of uncertainty. Consider then the interval of length L_j which remains after j experiments have been run. At one end of this interval is the recently rejected experiment E_j^-, and L_{j+1}^* units from the other end is the experiment E_j^+ with the highest outcome of all the first j experiments. Since in planning the experiments one had to allow for the possibility that E_j^- might be retained instead of E_j^+, the two trials E_j^+ and E_j^- must have been located symmetrically in the preceding interval of length L_{j-1}^*. This symmetry implies that E_j^- was L_{j+1}^* units from the nearest end of L_{j-1}^*. It follows that

$$L_{j-1}^* = L_j^* + L_{j+1}^* \qquad (2\text{-}8)$$

for all $1 < j < n$. Equation (2-6) is the special case which arises when $j = n - 1$.

Let us find some of the lengths L_j^* for j successively decreasing from $n - 1$. When $j = n - 2$ we have

$$L_{n-3}^* = L_{n-2}^* + L_{n-1}^* = (3L_n^* - \epsilon) + (2L_n^* - \epsilon)$$
$$= 5L_n^* - 2\epsilon$$

Similarly, $L_{n-4}^* = 8L_n^* - 3\epsilon$ and $L_{n-5}^* = 13L_n^* - 5\epsilon$.

In order to have a compact general formula for these lengths, let us introduce the sequence of numbers F_k, defined as

$$F_0 = F_1 = 1 \qquad (2\text{-}9a)$$
$$F_k = F_{k-1} + F_{k-2}, \qquad k = 2, 3, \cdots \qquad (2\text{-}9b)$$

The first 25 members of this sequence of numbers are given in the third column of Table 2-1. These numbers are plotted in Fig. 2-12. F_k is called the kth *Fibonacci number* for historical reasons we shall mention a little later.

In terms of Fibonacci numbers we may write

$$L_{n-k}^* = F_{k+1}L_n^* - F_{k-1}\epsilon \qquad (2\text{-}10)$$

Taking the length L_1^* of the original interval to be unity, we have

$$L_1^* \equiv 1 = F_n L_n^* - F_{n-2}\epsilon$$

from which we obtain the fraction L_n^* of the original interval that remains after n sequential experiments placed according to an optimal search plan.

$$L_n^* = \frac{1}{F_n} + \frac{F_{n-2}\epsilon}{F_n} \qquad (2\text{-}11)$$

This interval is smaller than the one obtainable by either Kiefer or Johnson,

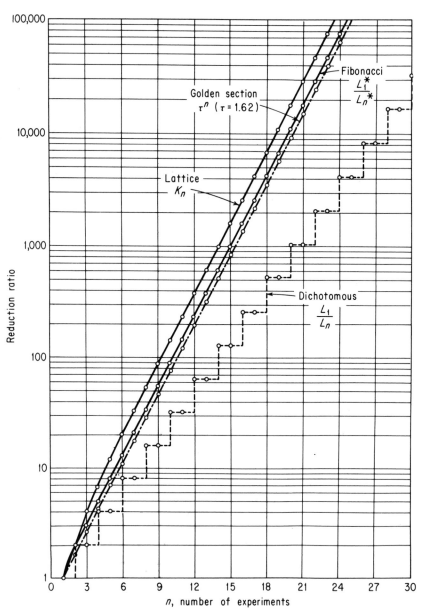

Fig. 2-12.

Table 2-1

REDUCTION RATIOS FOR VARIOUS SEQUENTIAL SEARCH PLANS

Number of Experiments	Dichotomous Search l_0/L_n	Fibonacci Search L_0/L_n*	Golden Section $(1.62)^{n-1}$	Lattice Search K_n
0	1	1		0
1	1	1	1	1
2	2	2	1.62	2
3	2	3	2.62	4
4	4	5	4.24	7
5	4	8	6.85	12
6	8	13	11.09	20
7	8	21	17.94	33
8	16	34	29.0	54
9	16	55	47.0	88
10	32	89	76.0	143
11	32	144	123	232
12	64	233	199	376
13	64	377	322	609
14	128	610	521	986
15	128	987	843	1596
16	256	1597	1364	2583
17	256	2584	2207	4180
18	512	4181	3570	6764
19	512	6765	5778	10945
20	1024	10946	9349	17710
21	1024	17711	15127	28656
22	2048	28657	24476	46367
23	2048	46368	39602	75024
24	4096	75025	64078	121392
25	4096	121393	103680	
26	8192			
27	8192			
28	16384			
29	16384			
30	32768			

namely $(1/F_n) + \epsilon$. This slight but sometimes significant improvement is due to L. T. Oliver.[†]

By this *Fibonacci search technique* an interval of uncertainty can be reduced to less than one per cent of its original length after only eleven sequential experiments (Table 2-1). As we pointed out earlier, this same reduction would require fourteen dichotomous experiments or 198 simultaneous trials.

[†] L. T. Oliver and D. J. Wilde, "Symmetric Sequential Minimax Search for a Maximum," *Chem. Eng. Dept. Techn. Report*, The University of Texas.

2.10. Placement of first experiment

Once a Fibonacci search has been begun, it is easy to decide what to do at each stage. Somewhere in each remaining interval of uncertainty will be a previous experiment. To continue the search, all one needs to do is locate the next experiment symmetrically with respect to the one already in the interval. Thus by specifying the location of the first experiment of the sequence we define the entire Fibonacci search technique.

The first Fibonacci experiment must be placed L_2^* units from one end of the original unit interval of uncertainty. It does not matter which end because of the method's symmetry. To obtain L_2^*, we simply write Eq. (2-10) for the case where $n - k = 2$.

$$L_2^* = F_{n-1}L_n^* - F_{n-3}\epsilon$$

Next we eliminate L_n^*, using Eq. (11).

$$L_2^* = \frac{F_{n-1}}{F_n} + \frac{(F_{n-1}F_{n-2} - F_nF_{n-3})\epsilon}{F_n} \qquad (2\text{-}12)$$

The coefficient of ϵ can be simplified considerably by substituting the identities $F_{n-1} \equiv F_{n-2} + F_{n-3}$ and $F_n \equiv F_{n-1} + F_{n-2}$ into its numerator.

$$F_{n-1}F_{n-2} - F_nF_{n-3} = (F_{n-2} + F_{n-3})F_{n-2} - (F_{n-1} + F_{n-2})F_{n-3}$$
$$= F_{n-2}^2 - F_{n-1}F_{n-3}$$

Two centuries ago, in an article with the remarkable title "An Explication of an Obscure Passage in Albert Girard's Commentary upon Simon Stevin's Works,"[†] R. Simson proved that the right side of the above equation is equal to $(-1)^n$, which may be verified by inspection of Table 2-1. This result will be derived in Sec. 2-13. Equation (2-12) may therefore be simplified considerably to obtain

$$L_2^* = \frac{F_{n-1}}{F_n} + \frac{(-1)^n\epsilon}{F_n} \qquad (2\text{-}13)$$

This is all we need to begin a Fibonacci search.

2.11. Rabbits

In spite of the newness of the optimal sequential search technique itself, the rather curious sequence of numbers associated with it has been known since the middle ages. H.S.M. Coxeter[‡] has written that "In 1202, Leonardo of Pisa, nicknamed Fibonacci (not 'son of an ass,' as has been

† *Phil. Trans. Roy. Soc. London,* **48.1** (1753), pp. 368–76.

‡ "The Golden Section, Phyllotaxis, and Wythoff's Game," *Scripta Mathematica* (1954) pp. 135–43. We are indebted to Professor R. E. Greenwood of The University of Texas for this reference.

suggested, but rather 'son of good nature' or 'prosperity'), came across his celebrated sequence of integers in connection with the breeding of rabbits." Although Professor Coxeter's intriguing parenthesis suggests that certain scholars of old Italian may have harbored doubts about Fibonacci's community stature, mathematicians today regard Fibonacci as a real pioneer in the study of infinite series.

Fibonacci speculated about rabbits that would take one month to mature and another to bring forth a litter. For the sake of simplicity, he assumed that one couple from each litter, along with their parents, were to be retained for future generations. He also required the replacement of any rabbits losing their fertility through death, sterility, or incompatibility. Fibonacci was hardly the first to find mathematical inspiration in the fecundity of domestic animals; the fable of the milkmaid counting her chickens before they are hatched antedates the Christian era.[†] But where his predecessors simply would have doubled the number of rabbits every two months, Fibonacci shrewdly took account of the ability of rabbits, once mature, to generate posterity each and every month.

Let F_n represent the number of *pairs* of rabbits alive at the end of n months according to Fibonacci's model. Starting with one pair of newborn rabbits, we see that there would be no increase during the first two months:

$$F_0 = F_1 = 1$$

In the nth month, F_{n-1} pairs of old rabbits from the preceding month would still be around in addition to F_{n-2} pairs of babies born to all the rabbits alive two months before. The total being defined as F_n, we have the recursion relation $F_n = F_{n-1} + F_{n-2}$ which, together with the initial conditions, generates the Fibonacci sequence 1, 1, 2, 3, 5, 8, 13, 21, 34 of Table 2-1.

For comparison, let R_n be the pairs of rabbits alive after n months as predicted by the simpler model involving one bi-monthly birth per couple. In this case the recursion relation is $R_n = 2R_{n-2}$, with, as in Fibonacci's model, $F_0 = F_1 = 1$. This gives $R_n = 2^{[n/2]}$, where $[n/2]$ is simply the greatest integer less than $n/2$. The doubling sequence is therefore 1, 1, 2, 2, 4, 4, 8, 8, 16, ... As one would expect, Fibonacci's estimate of the rabbit population after the second month always exceeds that of the simpler model: $F_n > R_n$ for $n > 2$.

To gain insight into just what makes the Fibonacci search technique better than the dichotomous method, we shall draw analogies between the effectiveness of sequential search plans and the growth of rabbit colonies. It is easy to see that the number of experiments in the former problem

[†] Joseph Jacobs, *The Fables of Aesop* (New York: The Macmillan Company, 1894), pp. 183 and 219.

corresponds to the number of generations in the latter (n has been used to denote both). Search schemes reduce a given interval of uncertainty to some fraction L_n of its original length, and we have been using L_n to measure the effectiveness of a search plan. The reciprocal $1/L_n$ represents then the length of the original interval of uncertainty which can be reduced to unit length after n experiments. This final interval of unit length corresponds to the original pair of rabbits, and $1/L_n$ to the total number of rabbits alive n months later. Neglecting the separation ϵ, we see that for a dichotomous search,

$$\frac{1}{L_n} = 2^{[n/2]}R_n$$

and so a dichotomous search is similar in form to the simple doubling model. Similarly, for a Fibonacci search we have

$$\frac{1}{L_n^*} = F_n$$

The optimal search plan corresponds therefore to Fibonacci's more sophisticated rabbit model.

Now we can see what it is about the Fibonacci search plan that makes it better than the dichotomous technique. In a Fibonacci scheme *each new experiment* serves to reduce the interval of uncertainty, just as each month sees new births among Fibonacci's rabbits. But in a dichotomous scheme it takes *two* new experiments to cut down the interval of uncertainty, just as the simplified rabbit model assumes births only in alternate months.

And so we see that, unlikely as it may have seemed at first, there really is a link between our modern search problem and the speculations of young Leonardo of Pisa. Thanks to him his native city will be remembered for other things than its famous Tower and its treacherous subsoil. Fibonacci's numbers turn up not only in other branches of mathematics, but even in such botanical phenomena as the arrangement of the scales on a pineapple! Those intrigued by games, puzzles, constructions, and paradoxes would find Professor Coxeter's article fascinating reading indeed.

2.12 The golden section

Often an experimenter begins searching for an optimum without knowing in advance exactly how many experiments to use. He simply keeps experimenting until the criterion of interest becomes good enough to satisfy him. But even when totally unconcerned about the interval of uncertainty itself, he would like to use a search plan that would rapidly close in on the optimum, since such a plan would reasonably give good values of the criterion as early as possible in the search.

Unfortunately, unless the number of experiments to be performed is known in advance, one cannot use the Fibonacci technique. This is because L_2^*, which must be known before the first experiment can be located, depends entirely on n, the number of trials [Eq. (2-13)]. One might be tempted to fall back on the dichotomous search method, which does not suffer from this defect. There is however another technique which, while nearly as effective as the Fibonacci method, is completely independent of the number of experiments available.

As before, let j represent the number of experiments already run. We may use the same reasoning as before to deduce that the experimental plan should place successive experiments such that, Eq. (2-8),

$$L_{j-1} = L_j + L_{j+1}$$

just as for the Fibonacci technique. This time, however, we cannot invoke the initial condition

$$L_{n-1} = 2L_n - \epsilon$$

since we do not known what n is. Let us instead hold the ratio of successive lengths constant. Calling this ratio τ, we have

$$\frac{L_{j-1}}{L_j} = \frac{L_j}{L_{j+1}} \equiv \tau$$

By dividing Eq. (2-8) throughout by L_{j+1} and noting that

$$\frac{L_{j-1}}{L_{j+1}} = \tau^2$$

we obtain $\tau^2 = \tau + 1$ as shown in Fig. 2-13. Only one root of this quadratic equation is positive, and so we see that

$$\tau = \frac{1 + \sqrt{5}}{2} = 1.618033989 \ldots \tag{2-14}$$

Notice that the negative root is $-1/\tau$. The results of the two experiments will determine which segment is to be explored further. As usual, this remaining segment will contain one of the previous trials, and to continue the search one merely places the next experiments symmetrically in the interval. Once begun, this process may be

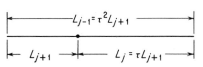

Fig. 2-13. The Golden Section.

continued as long as desired. After n experiments the interval L_n remaining is given by

$$L_n = 1/\tau^{n-1} \tag{2-15}$$

We shall call this procedure *search by golden section*.

Such a name requires justification. Although both Kiefer and Johnson have suggested the search technique just developed, the first man to divide a line segment as we have done here was none other than Euclid himself, and as one might expect, he did it entirely with ruler and compass (Euclid II, 11). Division of a segment into two unequal parts so that the ratio of the whole to the larger is equal to the ratio of the larger to the smaller came to be known as the *golden section*. Coxeter describes how the many surprising properties of this construction gave it great mystical significance among scholars of the Renaissance—Kepler ranked it with the Theorem of Pythagoras. Thus the venerable and respected "golden section" appears again in a modern application, and we thought it only right to combine old terminology with new in the name "search by golden section."

In order to compare the performance of the search by golden section with the Fibonacci method, we make use of the following relation[†] between the Fibonacci numbers and τ:

$$F_n = \frac{\tau^{n+1} - (-\tau)^{-(n+1)}}{\sqrt{5}} \tag{2-16}$$

This equation, to be derived in the next section, can be employed to prove Simson's result

$$F_{n-2}^2 - F_{n-1}F_{n-3} = (-1)^n$$

used in the derivation of Eq. (2-13) which showed how to begin a Fibonacci search. When n is very large the second term becomes negligible, giving approximately

$$F_n \approx \tau^{n+1}/\sqrt{5} \tag{2-17}$$

If L_n is the interval left after n trials in a search by golden section, and if L_n^* is that remaining after n Fibonacci experiments, then for large n

$$\frac{L_n}{L_n^*} = \frac{\tau^{n+1}}{\sqrt{5}\,\tau^{n-1}} = \frac{\tau^2}{\sqrt{5}} = 1.1708$$

Thus a search by golden section will give a final interval only about seventeen per cent longer than that obtainable by Fibonacci search (Table 2-1 and Fig. 2-12).

Lucas' formula also tells us that when n is large,

$$\frac{F_{n-1}}{F_n} \approx \frac{1}{\tau} \tag{2-18}$$

Combining Eq. (2-13) and (2-18) we have that for large n, $L_2^* \approx 1/\tau$. But

[†] E. Lucas, "Note sur l'application des séries récurrents à la recherche de la loi de distribution des nombres premiers," *Compt. rend. Acad. Sci. Paris*, **82** (1876), pp. 165–167.

by Eq. (2-15) $L_2 = 1/\tau$ for a search by golden section, and so when n is large both the Fibonacci technique and the search by golden section start practically at the same point. By examining Table 2-1 we see that the ratio of successive Fibonacci numbers approaches 0.618 very soon, and even for $n = 4$ the ratio is already 0.600—only 3 per cent low. We may therefore start a search using the golden section technique, switching to the Fibonacci method when we are sufficiently close to the optimum to fix the remaining number of experiments.

For example we could begin with an indefinite number of experiments, placing early trials according to the golden section. At some point in the search we might be able to predict that four more experiments should be sufficient. We then would place the next trial according to the Fibonacci plan for five experiments (counting the one already in the interval). In this way we would recover most of the efficiency of the Fibonacci technique, even though we had started out with absolutely no idea how many experiments would be needed.

2.13. The equation of Lucas†

Several of the results presented so far have been based on Lucas' equation relating the Fibonacci numbers to the golden section number τ.

$$F_n = \frac{\tau^{n+1} - (-\tau)^{-(n+1)}}{5}$$

We shall now derive this formula using methods applicable to solving any recurrence relation, of which the defining equation for the Fibonacci sequence is an example.

$$F_{n+2} = F_{n+1} + F_n, \qquad n = 0, 1, 2, \ldots \qquad (2\text{-}19)$$

Recurrence relations also arise in the analysis of diverse problems in inventory theory, sampled-data automatic control, genetics, multiple stage separation processes, and sequential decisions.

The nth Fibonacci number can be considered a function F_n of the non-negative integers $n = 0, 1, 2, \ldots$. Let us construct a power series whose terms are decreasing negative powers of a new parameter z. The coefficient of the ith term will be F_i, the ith Fibonacci number, so that the new function $F_n(z)$ is

$$F_n(z) = F_0 + F_1 z^{-1} + F_2 z^{-2} + F_3 z^{-3} + \cdots = \sum_{i=0}^{\infty} F_i z^{-i} \qquad (2\text{-}20)$$

The new function $F_n(z)$, which depends only on the parameter z, is called the "z-transform" of the original function F_n, the nth Fibonacci number.

† The inclusion of this section was suggested by Professor Oscar Kempthorne of Iowa State University.

Next we write the z-transform of ith $(n+1)$th Fibonacci number F_{n+1}. By definition the coefficient of the ith term will be F_{i+1}, and

$$F_{n+1}(z) = F_1 + F_2 z^{-1} + F_3 z^{-2} + F_4 z^{-3} + \cdots$$
$$= z[F_0 + F_1 z^{-1} + F_2 z^{-2} + \cdots] - zF_0 \qquad (2\text{-}21)$$
$$= z[F_n(z) - F_0]$$

Simply by advancing the index of this equation we obtain a relation between $F_{n+2}(z)$ and $F_{n+1}(z)$.

$$F_{n+2}(z) = z[F_{n+1}(z) - F_1]$$

Combining this with Eq. (2-21) and using the fact that $F_0 = F_1 = 1$, we obtain

$$F_{n+2}(z) = z^2 F_n(z) - z^2 - z \qquad (2\text{-}22)$$

Carrying out the z-transformation on both sides of equation (2-19), we find that

$$F_{n+2}(z) = F_{n+1}(z) + F_n(z)$$

This, together with Eqs. (2-21) and (2-22), gives a new expression for $F_n(z)$.

$$F_n(z) = \frac{z^2}{z^2 - z - 1} \qquad (2\text{-}23)$$

By synthetic division one can verify that

$$\frac{z^2}{z^2 - z - 1} = 1 + z^{-1} + 2z^{-2} + 3z^{-3} + 5z^{-4} + 8z^{-5} - \cdots$$

as required. The denominator of $F_n(z)$ has the same form as the equation defining the golden section, and so its roots are τ and $-\tau^{-1}$. Hence we may factor the denominator and perform a partial fraction expansion.

$$F(z) = \frac{z^2}{(z - \tau)(z + \tau^{-1})} = \frac{z^2}{\sqrt{5}}\left[\frac{1}{z - \tau} - \frac{1}{z + \tau^{-1}}\right]$$

The factor $1/\sqrt{5}$ comes from the fact that $\tau + \tau^{-1} = \sqrt{5}$. The two terms can be expanded into a geometric series in z^{-1}.

$$\frac{1}{z - \tau} = \frac{z^{-1}}{1 - \tau z^{-1}} = z^{-1}[1 + \tau z^{-1} + \tau^2 z^{-2} + \tau^3 \tau^{-3} + \cdots]$$

$$\frac{1}{z + \tau^{-1}} = \frac{z^{-1}}{1 + \tau^{-1}z^{-1}} = z^{-1}[1 - \tau^{-1}z^{-1} + \tau^{-2}z^{-2} - \tau^{-3}z^{-3} + \cdots]$$

It follows that

$$F_n(z) = \frac{1}{\sqrt{5}}\sum_{i=0}^{\infty}[\tau^{i+1} - (-\tau)^{-(i+1)}]z^{-1} = \sum_{i=0}^{\infty}F_i z^{-i}$$

By matching corresponding coefficients of the two series we obtain the equation of Lucas.

2.14. Maximum number of experiments

Even when the function is known to be unimodal it may not be possible to detect, in a physical problem, the difference between the outcomes of two measurements that are too close together. When this happens, the experimenter is unable to reduce the interval of uncertainty, and one of the observations is useless. Thus, in designing a sequential search technique, one must take into account the minimum spacing ϵ for which two outcomes are distinguishable. The smallest interval of uncertainty obtainable practically is therefore 2ϵ,

$$L_n = x_{j+1} - x_{j-1} = (x_{j+1} - x_j) - (x_j - x_{j-1}) = 2\epsilon. \qquad (2\text{-}24)$$

Although the resolution ϵ is usually negligible compared to the original interval of uncertainty, it is often a large fraction of the final interval L_n if the search is at all efficient.

The need for distinguishibility puts an upper bound on the number of experiments that can be performed profitably. Let m be this maximum number for a Fibonacci search. Equations (2-11) and (2-24) together give

$$L_m^* = \frac{1}{F_m} + \frac{F_{m-2}\epsilon}{F_m} \ge 2\epsilon,$$

from which one can show that

$$F_{m+1} \le \frac{1}{\epsilon} < F_{m+2} \qquad (2\text{-}25)$$

Thus if ϵ is only one per cent of 1, there is no advantage in performing more than nine experiments because $89 = F_{10} < 100 < F_{11} = 144$. When n is large, Lucas' relation (2-17) gives approximately

$$F_{m+1} \approx \frac{(1.618)^{m+2}}{\sqrt{5}}$$

which can be used to obtain, from Eq. (2-25),

$$m \le 4.785 \log \frac{1}{\epsilon} - 0.328 \qquad (2\text{-}26)$$

2.15. Lattice search

It is not rare to encounter search problems in which the independent variable x cannot vary continuously within the given interval of uncertainty, but is instead confined to a finite number of points. Such situations arise whenever x is restricted to integral values (1, 2, 3, *etc.*), as when one is deciding the optimal number of salesmen to assign to a territory, or the most profitable number of taxicabs to put into service in a large city. Even when the allowable values of x are not necessarily whole numbers, there may be only a finite number of possibilities to consider. In manning a sales territory, for example, one could arrange for a part-time salesman to work fewer than five days a week but not less than one day at a time. Although in this way one could speak of having a non-integral average number of salesmen on the force (5.4 for example), there would still be only a finite number of possibilities to consider.

The important characteristic of these *lattice search problems,* as Kiefer[†] calls them, is only that the number of points be finite and arrangeable in some order that will make the criterion of effectiveness unimodal. The points need not be uniformly spaced, and as long as there is some rational way to put them in order, they don't even have to be numbered. Suppose for instance that a new factory is to be built and that the technical group making the preliminary economic study is considering seven plant layouts which can be arranged in order of increasing complexity. If it can be assumed, based either on the form of the mathematical model describing the system, or on past experience with similar systems, that the net profit will be a unimodal function of the complexity of the plant, then one can treat the study of the seven cases as a lattice search problem. This is done simply by numbering the cases in order of increasing complexity.

Although the search techniques described so far are not appropriate for a lattice problem, they can be modified quite easily to suit this new application. We shall find, in fact, that sequential methods are in a sense even more effective with lattice problems than they were with the continuous problems already discussed. On the other hand, simultaneous search techniques are worthless on lattice problems, for only by placing an experiment at every point of the lattice could one be sure of finding the best point with a simultaneous search plan. Again we see the great advantage of sequential over simultaneous search plans.

Before showing how a lattice search should be performed, let us indicate why it may sometimes be advantageous to convert an ordinary continuous search into a lattice search *artificially.* When one is expected to make a decision based on the results of a search it is a bit frustrating to be confronted with an interval of uncertainty. A precise point would be preferable, since a specific decision is called for. One could, of course, choose a point at random in the final interval of uncertainty, but most

† J. Kiefer, "Optimum Sequential Search and Approximation Methods and Minimum Regularity Assumptions," *J. Soc. Ind. Appl. Math.* 5, 3 (Sept. 1957), p. 125.

people would prefer a point where a measurement had already been made. Once we have seen how the optimum lattice search technique works, it will be clear how to avoid these difficulties by converting the original problem into a lattice problem so that the final answer will be a specific point on which a firm decision can be based.

The sequential minimax scheme for lattice search problems can be developed much like that for a continuous variable, but we prefer to use here a rather clever derivation due to R.B. Cruz-Diaz, a student of ours. The search plan itself is due to Kiefer.

Let us associate the lattice points, whose total number we shall denote by K, with the integers 1 through K. Thus if we were to consider having 3.0, 3.2, 3.4, 4.0, 4.2, 4.4, or 5.0 men on the territory sales force, we would number the possibilities as shown in Table 2-2. The decimals allow for the possibility of having part-time salesmen. Notice that the original numbers are not equally spaced.

Table 2-2

CASE NUMBERING

Number of salesmen	3.0	3.2	3.4	4.0	4.2	4.4	5.0
Case number	1	2	3	4	5	6	7

Next we space the K points uniformly in the interval running from zero to $K + 1$ as shown in Fig. 2-14(b). Suppose that the length $K + 1$ just happened to be equal to one of the Fibonacci numbers, say, F_n. Although such a special case would certainly be something of a coincidence, we shall study this particular situation first and find out later how to handle the general case. In Fig. 2-14, where $K = 7$, the length of the associated interval of uncertainty is 8, which is of course the Fibonacci number F_5.

Let us begin to narrow down the associated interval of uncertainty as efficiently as possible, that is, by means of a Fibonacci search. Equation (2-13), repeated below, gives the distance L_2^* from one end of an original interval of unit length to the first Fibonacci experiment.

$$L_2^* = \frac{F_{n-1}}{F_n} + \frac{(-1)^n \epsilon}{F_n} \qquad (2\text{-}13)$$

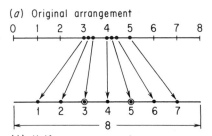

(a) Original arrangement

(b) Uniform arrangement
(Circled points represent first two Fibonacci experiments)

(c) Interval remaining after $n-1$ $(=4)$ Fibonacci experiments

Fig. 2-14. Lattice search on seven points.

Since we are dealing here with an original interval of length F_n, the first two experiments must be $F_n L_2^*$ units from the ends. Now if we take ϵ to be zero we have

$$F_n L_2^* = F_{n-1}$$

Thus the first two experiments for a Fibonacci search will coincide with points of the original lattice. In Fig. 2-14 for example, the first experiments would be F_4, or 5, units from each end—exactly at points 5 and 3.

Since the length of the interval remaining is also a Fibonacci number, we see that the third experiment will also fall on one of the lattice points. This procedure may be continued until n experiments have been used up and the length of the interval of uncertainty is down to $F_n L_n^*$, which by Eq. (2-11) is simply one unit when ϵ is zero.

$$F_n L_n^* = 1$$

The last experiment will, of course, be at the optimal lattice point.

In the preceding analysis there was, however, a note of artificiality introduced by our taking the minimum separation ϵ to be zero. The perceptive reader will notice that because of this assumption, the last experiment must necessarily coincide with one of those already run and that there is in fact no need to perform it at all. To verify this, let us examine the interval of uncertainty remaining after $n - 1$ experiments have been run. According to Eq. (2-5), its length $F_n L_{n-1}^*$ will be two units long, and there will be one previous experiment exactly at its mid-point, as shown in Fig. 2-14(c). Let j be the number of this lattice point. The interval of uncertainty runs *between* the adjacent lattice points $j - 1$ and $j + 1$, but it does not include them because they have already been eliminated as possible locations for the optimum. Thus $(j - 1) < x^* < (j + 1)$, and j is the only lattice point left in the interval. It follows that j must be the best of all the original lattice points.

Let the maximum number of points which can be narrowed down to a single optimum in $n - 1$ experiments be denoted by K_{n-1}. The above argument has shown that an interval of length F_n, containing $F_n - 1$ lattice points, can be searched by the Fibonacci technique to find the best lattice point in $n - 1$ experiments. Hence

$$K_{n-1} = F_n - 1$$

or equivalently,

$$K_n = F_{n+1} - 1 \qquad (2\text{-}27)$$

This maximum number of lattice points that can be searched sequentially in n experiments is given in the fifth column of Table 2-1 and in Fig. 2-12.

Now we can decide what to do when the number K of lattice points does not happen to be exactly one less than a Fibonacci number, that is, when $K_{n-1} < K < K_n$. We need only add enough fictitious lattice points to the original set to bring the total up to K_n and then proceed as before. It is convenient, although not essential, to put the fictitious points at the ends of the interval rather than between points of the original set. In summary, to search a set of lattice points, simply arrange them in a continuous interval in such a way that Fibonacci experiments for the interval will coincide with the lattice points.

As we suggested earlier, when one wants to base a specific decision on the outcome of a search, it may be worthwhile to convert a continuous search to a lattice search. To do this one must pick n, the number of experiments, and then commence a Fibonacci search as if it involved $n + 1$ experiments with no separation allowance ($\epsilon = 0$). The sequence is stopped after n trials have been made, and the point giving the best value is taken as the optimum. All decisions are then based on this precise point.

2.16. Randomization

In the preceding section we showed how to apply the Fibonacci search technique to criteria of effectiveness defined on a discrete set of points. Whenever the number of points happens to be exactly one less than a Fibonacci number, the Fibonacci scheme is quite straightforward. In other cases we suggested adding fictitious points to the original set until the total is one less than a Fibonacci number and then proceeding with a Fibonacci scheme. This proposal is safe, simple, and quite effective. But there is in fact another scheme which, while just as safe as the method of fictitious points, is slightly more efficient. This new technique, called *randomization*, may seem strange to most engineering and science students seeing it for the first time, and anyone too confused by it can always fall back on the method of fictitious points. The purpose of this section is not so much to show how to improve the efficiency of the already highly effective method of fictitious points, but rather to introduce the somewhat unconventional notion of randomization, which has many potential applications to practical decision problems.

Randomization involves letting certain decisions be decided by *chance* —the flip of a coin, the fall of a die, or a number drawn from a hat. This may seem a bit unprofessional, if not downright shady, to anyone unversed in the theory of probability and statistics. Randomization is, however, quite respectable, and it certainly deserves discussion in a book on optimization, especially since the concept of randomization is allied to that of a *mixed strategy* in game theory. No previous knowledge of probability theory is needed to understand this useful concept.

Before discussing randomization itself we shall consider how one can improve upon the method of fictitious points simply by taking advantage of any experiment-saving opportunities that might present themselves. Specifically, suppose we are seeking the maximum of a function defined on eight discrete points ($K = 8$). The next higher Fibonacci number being 13, we must add four fictitious points to the original set to bring the total up to 12. Since 13 is the fifth Fibonacci number F_5, we would expect our method to find the maximum in five experiments. We shall see that under certain circumstances we can find it in four, or if we are really fortunate, in three.

Let the original points be numbered 1 through 8, and let the fictitious points be added to the left end and numbered 9 through 12 as in Fig. 2-15. The first two experiments are to be performed at points 5 and 8 in accordance with the Fibonacci technique. Now if the criterion is greater at 5 than at 8, all of the dummy points as well as point 8 itself will be eliminated (Fig. 2-15(b)), leaving seven original points in position for a further Fibonacci search which will terminate after three more experiments—five in all. On the other hand if the criterion is greater at 8 than at 5, only *three* original points are left (Fig. 2-15(c)), which will certainly take no more than two more experiments to search. In this case at most four experiments are required to locate the maximum. By being alert to such opportunities an experimenter can decrease the total number of trials needed below the ceiling guaranteed by the Fibonacci technique.

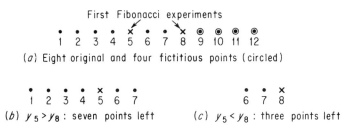

Fig. 2-15. Lattice search on eight points.

This occasional improvement over the method of fictitious points suggests the existence of methods which might automatically take advantage of good fortune without running undue risks. Kiefer[†] has shown that *randomization* does this and is indeed the best possible search technique whenever the number of lattice points is not precisely one less than a Fibonacci number. We shall now show how randomization works and why it is effective.

† J. Kiefer, "Optimum Sequential Search and Approximation Methods under Minimum Regularity Assumptions," *J. Soc. Ind. Appl. Math.* 5, 3 (Sept. 1957) p. 125.

Consider first a unimodal function defined on three discrete points numbered 1, 2, and 3 from left to right. Where should we place the first two experiments? There are three possibilities: $(1, 2)$, $(1, 3)$, and $(2, 3)$, where for example $(1, 2)$ stands for the decision to make the first trials at points 1 and 2. If the optimum happened to be at point 1, then a third experiment would not be required for the choice $(1, 2)$. Similarly, whenever the optimum is at point 3 and we have decided to run the first experiments at $(2, 3)$, no third experiment would be needed. For any other combination of circumstances, all three points would have to be tested. The nine possibilities are displayed in Table 2-3.

Table 2-3

NUMBER OF TRIALS REQUIRED TO FIND OPTIMUM

Location of First Two Experiments	Location of Optimum		
	1	2	3
$(1, 2)$	2	3	3
$(1, 3)$	3	3	3
$(2, 3)$	3	3	2

Let us see if the minimax concept will help us decide what to do. According to the minimax approach we would pretend that the location of the optimum is being selected by a clever, malevolent opponent who wishes to maximize the number of experiments we'll need to find the optimum. He doesn't know which choice we'll make, and we know nothing of his plans. We would be foolish to elect $(1, 3)$, since this would always lead to a third experiment no matter where the optimum happened to be. Unfortunately our hypothetical adversary has us at a disadvantage, for by placing the optimum at point 2 he can force us to use three experiments every time. Thus the minimax concept, although enabling us to eliminate one choice, is too conservative to distinguish between the two remaining.

In reality of course there is no intelligent opponent—the location of the optimum is not at all influenced by our desire to find it with as few experiments as possible. Hence, it is unwise to be over-concerned with the worst possible location, namely point 2. We should instead try to do our best with the other two locations, which offer some hope of finding the optimum in less than three trials. Suppose then that we ignore the possibility of the optimum's being at point 2. This would certainly be reckless if any of the numbers in column 2 were greater than 3, for then we would be shutting our eyes to the worst of all the nine possible outcomes. But here 3, the highest number in column 2, is no greater than the largest number in any other column. Thus by ignoring column 2 entirely we make possible the exploitation of the two-trial possibilities without risking having to perform more than three experiments if things go wrong.

With the choices (1, 3) and 2 eliminated from further consideration, only the four possible outcomes shown in Table 2-4 remain. To choose between (1, 2) and (2, 3) is simply impossible; in both cases the maximum number of experiments one might need is three and the minimum is two. Faced with two alternatives as indistinguishable as these, the soberest of men would be tempted to flip a coin to break the tie, and this is exactly what we propose to do.

Table 2-4

NUMBER OF TRIALS REQUIRED
TO FIND OPTIMUM

Location of First Two Experiments	Location of Optimum 1	3
(1, 2)	2	3
(2, 3)	3	2

We associate "heads" with one choice, say (1, 2) and "tails" with the other. The result of the coin flip tells us which alternative to take. Since for a fair coin the probability of "heads" is the same as that of "tails," we are in effect defining a policy which in the long run chooses (1, 2) about half the time and (2, 3) the other half. If we let p be the *probability* that (1, 2) will be chosen, then when the random element is a coin, $p = \frac{1}{2}$. The probability of choosing (2, 3) is in general $1 - p$, or one half in this case. This use of a random device to decide what to do is what we mean by *randomization*. Although randomization may seem more like avoiding a decision than making one, there is theoretical justification for randomization which we shall now develop.

2.17 Mixed strategy

The idea of flipping a coin to decide between two identical alternatives has strong intuitive appeal because a coin has two sides, one for each choice. In general however we could have used any random device, a single die for example, with probabilities not equal to one half. Suppose for instance that we associated the decision (1, 2) with the die face 1 and the decision (2, 3) with the die faces 2, 3, 4, 5, and 6. Then the probability p of selecting (1, 2) would be $\frac{1}{6}$ instead of $\frac{1}{2}$, and the probability $(1 - p)$ of selecting (2, 3) would be $\frac{5}{6}$. Although it would seem more reasonable to have the two probabilities p and $(1 - p)$ equal, we have not yet justified this conjecture.

Let us now treat p as a variable ranging from zero to unity and find the particular probability $p*$ which is best in some sense. Suppose we were to perform the search a large number of times. Let n_1 stand for the number of times the optimum turns out to be at point 1. Using our random device, we would select $(1, 2)$ about $n_1 p$ times, each time finding the optimum in only two experiments. The other $n_1(1 - p)$ times we would have chosen $(2, 3)$ and needed three experiments each time. Thus the total number of experiments would be $2n_1 p + 3n_1(1 - p)$. Dividing this total by n_1 we obtain e_1, the average (or expected) number of experiments performed for our randomized search *when the optimum is really at point 1.*

$$e_1 = 2p + 3(1 - p) = 3 - p$$

Next let n_3 be the number of times the optimum turns out to be at point 3. This time the total number of experiments would be $3n_3 p + 2n_3(1 - p)$, and the expected number e_3 of experiments performed when the optimum is really at point 3 would be given by

$$e_3 = 3p + 2(1 - p) = 2 + p$$

Let us now use the minimax concept on those expected values, e_1 and e_3, seeking the value of p minimizing the function max $\{(3 - p), (2 + p)\}$. This function attains its minimum value of 2.5 for $p* = \frac{1}{2}$. Thus

$$p* = 1 - p*$$

and we should flip a coin just as our intuition told us.

The number 2.5 is the expected number of experiments to be performed when the optimum is either at point 1 or 3 .To take account of the possibility of the optimum's being at point 2, let n_2 be the number of times this happens. For abbreviation, define

$$f_i \equiv n_i/(n_1 + n_2 + n_3) \qquad \text{for } i = 1, 2, 3$$

as the *frequency* with which the optimum is at point i. Then $e*$, the average number of experiments for the minimax randomized search plan, is given by

$$e* = 2.5(1 - f_2) + 3f_2$$
$$= 2.5 + 0.5f_2 \tag{2-28}$$

In the preceding analysis the frequencies were unknown, and the minimax concept led to a randomized strategy requiring the lowest average number of experiments for a given frequency f_2. This average was in fact totally independent of the relative sizes of f_1 and f_3. Thus even if f_i were being selected by a crafty opponent trying to make us run as many experiments as possible, we can keep the average number of experiments at $e*$ no matter what he does, provided, of course, that f_2 is held constant.

Suppose however that the frequencies f_i could be estimated in advance. We shall see that in this case the average number of experiments can be reduced if we take advantage of this new information. Noting that

$$f_2 = 1 - f_1 - f_3 \tag{2-29}$$

we may write the following expression for e, the average number of experiments performed, as a function of p, f_1, and f_3:

$$\begin{aligned} e &= (3 - p)f_1 + 3(1 - f_1 - f_3) + (2 + p)f_3 \\ &= 3 - f_3 + p(f_3 - f_1) \end{aligned} \tag{2-30}$$

This quantity is minimized by choosing $p = 1$ whenever f_1 exceeds f_3. If $f_1 = f_3$ the choice of p is immaterial. Formally,

$$p = \begin{cases} 0 & \text{when } f_1 \leq f_3 \\ 1 & \text{when } f_1 \geq f_3 \end{cases} \tag{2-31a}$$

and

$$e = \begin{cases} 3 - f_3 & \text{when } f_1 \leq f_3 \\ 3 - f_1 & \text{when } f_1 \geq f_3 \end{cases} \tag{3-31b}$$

By combining Eqs. (2-29), (2-30), and (2-31) we obtain the difference

$$e^* - e = \tfrac{1}{2}|f_1 - f_3| \geq 0$$

which represents the improvement over the randomized strategy. Thus when the frequencies f can be predicted, the choice between $(1, 2)$ and $(2, 3)$ is no longer random.

In the terminology of game theory[†] each of the choices $(1, 2)$, $(1, 3)$, and $(2, 3)$ would be called a *pure strategy*. The randomized procedure which chooses among these pure strategies with probabilities $\tfrac{1}{2}$, 0, and $\tfrac{1}{2}$ is an example of *mixed strategy*.

2.18. Dominance

The preceding example was too simple to illustrate very many of the factors involved in finding a good randomized search strategy. Therefore let us turn to the problem of seeking the optimum among five points. For each of the ten possible placements of the first two experiments, Table 2-5 shows the maximum number of experiments required to find the optimum at its five possible locations. In constructing this table we assumed that after the first two trials have been made the rest of the search is conducted as efficiently as possible. But whenever a particular strategy could have more than one outcome, we always chose the worst.

---

† J. D. Williams, *op. cit. See also* J. Von Neumann and O. Morgenstern, *Theory of Games and Economic Behavior* (Princeton: Princeton University Press, 1944).

Table 2-5

MAXIMUM NUMBER OF TRIALS REQUIRED TO FIND OPTIMUM

Location of First Two Experiments	Location of Optimum				
	1	2	3	4	5
(1, 2) xx...	2	3	4	5	5
(1, 3) x.x..	3	4	4	4	4
(1, 4) x..x.	3	4	4	4	4
(1, 5) x...x	3	4	5	4	3
(2, 3) .xx..	3	3	3	4	4
(2, 4) .x.x.	3.5	4	3.5	4	3.5
(2, 5) .x..x	4	4	4	4	3
(3, 4) ..xx.	4	4	3	3	3
(3, 5) ..x.x	4	4	4	4	3
(4, 5) ...xx	5	5	4	3	2

Take strategy $(1, 3)$ for instance. When the optimum is really at point 2 there is no way to tell in advance whether $y_1 > y_3$ or $y_1 < y_3$. If the optimum sought were a maximum we would consider only the case where $y_1 < y_3$, for this would require two additional experiments. In the other case only one more would be needed.

The non-integral entries for pure strategy $(2, 4)$ require explanation. Consider for example the situation when the optimum is really at point 1. After the first two experiments only points 1, 2, and 3 will remain to be considered, and there will already be an experiment at point 2. We have just shown that in this case one should locate the next experiment either at 1 or at 3, using a random device to choose between them with equal probability. Half the time we would put the third experiment at point 1 and the search would terminate. The other half of the time we would locate it at point 3 and then be forced to test point 1 before ending the search. On the average, therefore, 3.5 experiments would be needed. A similar argument obtains when the optimum is at point 3 or point 5.

To simplify the problem we must now eliminate as may of these possibilities as we can. It would certainly be rash to use strategies $(1, 2)$, $(1, 5)$, or $(4, 5)$, because they carry the risk of having to explore all five points while even the method of fictitious points would protect us from ever having to explore more than four. Strategy $(2, 3)$ is always as good or better than strategies $(1, 3)$ and $(1, 4)$, no matter where the optimum happens to be, and it is therefore unprofitable to consider $(1, 3)$ and $(1, 4)$ further. In game theory terminology, $(2, 3)$ is said to *dominate* $(1, 3)$ and $(1, 4)$. Table 2-5 also shows that $(2, 5)$ and $(3, 5)$ are dominated by $(3, 4)$. Table 2-6 gives the three pure strategies that remain to us when the reckless and the dominated strategies are eliminated. Our

Table 2-6

THREE-BY-FIVE GAME

Location of First	Location of Optimum				
Two Experiments	1	2	3	4	5
(2, 3) .xx..	3	3	3	4	4
(2, 4) .x.x.	3.5	4	3.5	4	3.5
(3, 4) ..xx.	4	4	3	3	3

"opponent" having five strategies, Table 2-6 describes what is known as a *three-by-five game.*

Notice that unlike the three point situation there is no clear-cut pure strategy available to our hypothetical adversary by which he could force us to explore all five, or even four, points every time. From a clever opponent's viewpoint, however, strategy 2 dominates strategy 1, and 4 dominates 5. We can therefore simplify the problem further by disregarding the weaker strategies 1 and 5 of our fictitious opponent, leaving the three-by-three game of Table 2-7.

Table 2-7

REDUCED THREE-BY-THREE GAME

Location of First	Location of Optimum		
Two Experiments	2	3	4
(2, 3)	3	3	4
(2, 4)	4	3.5	4
(3, 4)	4	3	3

Since this game has no saddlepoint as did the game on page 17, the strategies of the "adversaries" do not coincide and we must randomize. Let p_{23}, p_{24}, and p_{34} represent the probabilities with which we are to select strategies $(2, 3)$, $(2, 4)$, and $(3, 4)$ respectively. For each location i of the optimum the expected number of experiments e_i will be

$$e_2 = 3p_{23} + 4p_{24} + 4p_{34}$$
$$e_3 = 3p_{23} + 3.5p_{24} + 3p_{34}$$
$$e_4 = 4p_{23} + 4p_{24} + 3p_{34}$$

The probabilities must sum to unity, and we may simplify by substituting

$$p_{24} = 1 - p_{23} - p_{34} \tag{2-32}$$

into these equations, obtaining

$$e_2 = 4 \qquad\quad - p_{23} \tag{2-33a}$$
$$e_3 = 3.5 - 0.5p_{23} - 0.5p_{34} \tag{2-33b}$$
$$e_4 = 4 \qquad\qquad\quad - p_{34} \tag{2-33c}$$

All of the quantities are decreased by making p_{23} and p_{34} as large as possible, which by Eq. (2-32) implies that

$$p_{24} = 0 \qquad (2\text{-}34)$$

and

$$p_{34} = 1 - p_{23} \qquad (2\text{-}35)$$

Combining Eqs. (2-33b), (2-33c), and (2-35) we obtain

$$e_3 = 3 \qquad (2\text{-}33\text{d})$$
$$e_4 = 3 + p_{23} \qquad (2\text{-}33\text{e})$$

Equations (2-33a), (2-33d), and (2-33e) show that the function max $\{e_2, e_3, e_4\}$ attains its minimum when

$$p_{23} = p_{34} = \tfrac{1}{2} \qquad (2\text{-}36)$$

The mixed strategy is therefore to place one experiment in the middle (at point 3) and then to locate another one next to the first one, flipping a coin to decide whether to put it on the left or on the right. The expected number of experiments needed for each of the five possible locations of the optimum is given in Table 2-8. The minimax value is 3.5. It can be shown that if the frequencies f_i of the optimum's being at location i can be estimated in advance, pure strategy (2, 3) should be chosen whenever $(f_1 + f_2) > (f_4 + f_5)$. Naturally when the inequality is reversed and the optimum has a greater chance of being on the right than on the left, pure strategy (3, 4) should be selected.

Table 2-8
EXPERIMENTS NEEDED FOR MINIMAX MIXED STRATEGY

	i, Location of Optimum				
	1	2	3	4	5
e_i, average number of experiments needed	3.5	3.5	3.25	3.5	3.5

When there are six points the optimal strategy is pure rather than mixed. One merely places the first two experiments at the two middle points 3 and 4. This will always leave three points with an old experiment at one end. The third experiment is therefore located at the middle point of the three remaining. If the optimum happens to be at the old experiment, then a fourth experiment is unnecessary, as illustrated in Fig. 2-16.

For seven points one employs, of course, a Fibonacci search. When there are eight, only the third experiment is randomized. The first two experiments are placed at points 3 and 6, which will always leave five points for further exploration. Since the old experiment is always at the

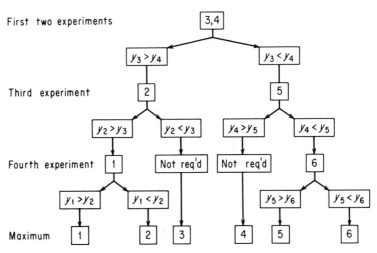

Fig. 2-16. Search plan for six points.

middle one of the five remaining, we have precisely the five-point case already analyzed. Hence the third experiment is put next to the old one, a coin toss determining whether the right one or the left one is to be selected.

A nine-point search is completely deterministic, the first two experiments being placed at points 3 and 7. This will leave six points to be searched in the way we have already outlined in Fig. 2-16. Similarly, for a ten-point search the first two points always should be at points 4 and 7, which again reduces to a six-point search.

Randomized placement of the first two points is called for when there are eleven points. One should mix the strategies $(4, 7)$ and $(5, 8)$ equally. At worst seven points would be left, with one old experiment in position for a Fibonacci search. With luck, however, only six points would remain, and the old experiment would be in the right place for the six-point search of Fig. 2-16. For twelve points a Fibonacci plan can be used.

In closing we reiterate that presentation of efficient search plans was only a secondary objective of this section, the savings involved being relatively slight. One can usually do almost as well by using the method of fictitious points and keeping alert for any testing economies that might turn up by chance. More important than search efficiency was the concept of randomization or mixed strategy. We have shown why it works and demonstrated how one can analyze situations where it might be applicable. The solutions for more complicated problems involving mixed strategy may be solved by linear programming.

EXERCISES

1. Prove that all convex functions are unimodal.

2. Find a cubic function of x which is unimodal but not convex for $0 \leq x \leq 1$.

3. The results of an eight experiment simultaneous search plan are given in the following table. The interval explored is $2 \leq x \leq 12$.

   x, independent variable 3.1 4.2 5.0 6.5 7.1 8.8 9.5 10.5
   y, dependent variable   1.0 1.5 3.2 3.0 2.6 2.3 1.9   1.4

   (a) What are the possible final intervals of uncertainty?
   (b) What is the length of the actual final interval of uncertainty in this case?
   (c) What is the length of the maximum possible interval of uncertainty?

4. Assuming that the outcomes of experiments are indistinguishable when closer to each other than 0.3 units, design a minimax eight experiment simultaneous search plan for the preceding exercise. What is the length of the maximum possible interval of uncertainty?

5. You are convinced that your optimization professor is trying to fail you if he can get enough evidence to do so. You are trying to decide whether or not to read the assignment for next Thursday. If you read it and the professor gives a ten minute quiz, you can expect to gain 10 points toward your final average. If there is no quiz, the knowledge you gained by reading the assignment will probably give you an extra five points on the next hour exam. You may go to the movies instead, and if there is no optimization quiz you will have three points worth of relaxation. But if there is a quiz and you haven't studied, your score will be zero for the day and the movie will be no consolation. What should be your minimax decision? If your professor is really out to get you what will he do?

6. Search for the maximum of the function $y = 3 + 6x - 4x^2$ in the interval $0 \leq x \leq 1$ with four sequential experiments. Space all experiments at least 0.05 unit apart. What is the length of the final interval? What is the highest value of y attained?

7. Conduct the same search as in Ex. 6 with four lattice experiments. What is the highest value of y attained?

8. Could the preceding search have been conducted efficiently with five experiments? Why?

9. Verify Lucas' relation, Eq. (2-16), for $n = 0$, $n = 1$, and $n = 2$.

10. Prove the approximation (2-17).

11. Using as few experiments as possible, explore the function $y = 4 - 3x + 5x^2$ in the interval $0 \leq x \leq 1$ until the value of y is less than 3.56. The experiments may be placed as close as desired, since one may always distinguish between two results by evaluating y to enough decimal places.

12. A medical research team is seeking the American with the highest concentration of exogen in the blood stream. Exogen concentration is known to be a unimodal function depending only on the date of birth of the individual, which is known to the team through U. S. Census Bureau records. What would be the least number of Americans that the team could examine and still find the one with the highest exogen content? Compare this figure to the number required if a dichotomous search were used.

13. Toward the end of a lattice search an experimenter knows that the minimum sought is at one of the four points $x_1 = -0.5$, $x_2 = 1.3$, $x_3 = 2.0$, or $x_4 = 2.9$. He has already found the output at x_4 to be 8.95. Where should he conduct the next experiment?

14. Verify that the search strategy suggested for six lattice experiments is best in the minimax sense.

15. Suppose in Ex. 5 that you have a third alternative, namely to study for an exam in another course. If then there is no optimization quiz, you can at least pick up eight points in your other course. But if your optimization professor gives a quiz, your zero in optimization will bring your average gain for the day down to four points. What should be your minimax strategy?

16. Suppose your optimization professor gives ten minute tests in approximately one third of his lectures, but as far as you can tell, entirely at random. What should be your minimax strategy?

17. Using Lucas' Eq. (2-16), prove that
$$F_{n-2}^2 - F_{n-1}F_{n-3} = (-1)^n,$$
a result needed to establish Eq. (2-13).

18. Show that the negative root of Eq. (2-14) is $-1/\tau$.

The Geometry of Multidimensional Response Surfaces

3

We turn now to the study of search problems in which the criterion of effectiveness depends on two or more independent variables. There are two principal ways of studying such functions. The more general method involves expressing the dependent variable in terms of the independent variables, using algebraic equations. According to this approach all analysis of the function is carried out by studying the equations. A second technique is to represent the function graphically, using Cartesian coordinates. This latter method often can give deep insight into the nature of the function because it brings to bear the geometric intuition and visual experience more or less well developed in all of us. Unfortunately graphical techniques are not practical when there are more than two independent variables. Thus we face the unhappy choice between geometric methods which are intuitively appealing but powerless to handle large numbers of variables, and algebraic methods which are generally applicable but difficult to visualize.

A compromise is definitely in order. We shall develop an algebraic apparatus of general applicability, each algebraic concept being illustrated geometrically for the special case in which there are exactly two independent variables. In this three-dimensional context such geometric ideas as tangent, contour, gradient, curvature, and perpendicularity are easier to visualize than their algebraic counterparts. Once the algebra for two independent variables is understood it can be extended quite simply to the general case, using the geometric concepts as a guide. Or, from another point of view, the geometric relations holding in three dimensions can be generalized readily in terms of their algebraic analogs.

Chapter 4 on multivariable strategies will depend heavily on the geometric concepts and algebraic techniques developed here. But this does not mean this chapter is unconcerned with experimental optimization. The methods for beginning and ending a multivariable search are so tied in with geometry that they will be discussed here rather than in Chap. 4, which will be confined to procedures applicable to the middle of a search.

An understanding of functions of many variables is useful not only for experimental optimization, but for many other topics in applied science as well. Indeed, one would be hard put to find in the complicated modern world a problem of any importance involving a function of a single variable. Most of the simple problems solvable by the graphical techniques so characteristic of basic engineering and economic analysis have already been solved. It therefore behooves us to know something about the behavior of systems of many variables, especially since high speed computers are now available to handle the calculations. Since multidimensional geometry is rarely discussed in college analytic geometry and calculus courses, at least in the United States, we must devote some time here to this rather elementary but exceedingly practical topic. Fortunately the few simple concepts needed can be developed quickly and without much effort.

3.01. Isometric projection

It is difficult, using only line drawings on the flat pages of a book, to describe solid objects, but this is exactly what we shall have to do before we can discuss the geometry of curves and surfaces in space. The isometric projection technique, with which most engineers are already familiar, will be employed because of its simplicity and good pictorial qualities. Isometric projection consists of representing three axes, mutually perpendicular in space, by a vertical line and two slanted lines as shown in Fig. 3-1. The slanted lines stand for the axes which are horizontal in space, while the vertical line corresponds to the axis vertical in space. The independent variables, denoted x_1 and x_2, are plotted parallel to these horizontal axes, and values of the dependent variable y (the criterion of effectiveness) are measured vertically above the x_1-x_2 plane.

In Fig. 3-1, the point **p** (notice the use of **boldface** type to denote points or vectors) has the coordinates $x_1 = 3$, $x_2 = 2$, and $y = 5.9$. Thus any ordered triplet of values $(x_1, x_2; y)$ can be represented graphically by a point in an isometric projection. The set of points corresponding to all possible ordered triplets forms a space of three dimensions. There are exactly *three* dimensions because at least three independent measurements, one for each coordinate, must be known to fix the location of a point.

Suppose y stands for a criterion in which we are interested which is a function of two independent variables x_1 and x_2.

$$y = y(x_1, x_2)$$

In this case not all of the points in the three-dimensional space satisfy the relation. Those that do will lie on a surface floating in the space as in Fig. 3-2, where the particular function depicted is

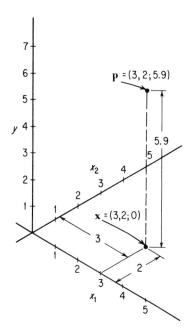

Fig. 3-1. Isometric representation of a point in space.

$$y = 5 - 0.2(x_1 - 3)^2 + 0.1(x_2 + 1)^2 \qquad (3\text{-}1)$$

The lines $x_1 = 0, 1, 2, 3, 4$ and $x_2 = 0, 1, 2, 3, 4$ have been drawn in the x_1-x_2 plane $(y = 0)$ and projected onto the surface to make it easier to visualize. Notice that the point **p**, already shown in Fig. 3-1, satisfies Eq. (3-1) and therefore lies on the surface. It is marked with a heavy dot at the intersection of $x_1 = 3$ with $x_2 = 2$ on the surface.

3.02. Response surfaces

Biologists and statisticians, for whom the criterion y is often the response of a living organism to environmental factors x_1 and x_2, have come to call surfaces of this sort *response surfaces*, a name which has recently found its way into engineering terminology because of the industrial applications of the work of G.E.P. Box.[†] The response surface of Fig. 3-2 is a two-dimensional object, because only two coordinates are needed to specify a point on it. For example, we may locate point **p** simply by

† G. E. P. Box, "The Exploration and Exploitation of Response Surfaces," *Biometrics,* 10 (1954).

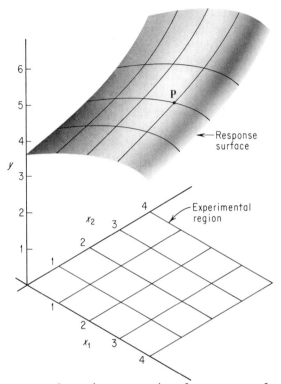

Fig. 3-2. Isometric representation of a response surface.

stating that it lies on the response surface and then giving the two co-ordinates $x_1 = 3$ and $x_2 = 2$. This corresponds to the algebraic operation of finding y at the point **p** by substituting the values of x_1 and x_2 into Eq. (3-1).

In algebraic terminology the difference between the number of variables and the number of independent equations relating them is called the *number of degrees of freedom*. For the response surface there are three variables (x_1, x_2, and y) linked by Eq. (3-1), leaving two degrees of freedom. Since the number of degrees of freedom equals the number of coordinates which must be fixed to determine a point, it is the same as the number of dimensions. Therefore the space of all possible points (x_1, x_2; y) not necessarily satisfying Eq. (3-1) has three degrees of freedom, or dimensions, while the response surface has only two. Geometrically speaking, a surface is a two-dimensional object imbedded in a three-dimensional space. For that matter, so is the x_1-x_2 plane on which $y = 0$, and the vertical plane on which $x_1 = 0$.

The intersection of two surfaces is a curve, which is one-dimensional.

This is because each surface is the representation of one equation relating the three variables. Points on the intersection belong to both surfaces and therefore must satisfy both equations, leaving only one degree of freedom. The space curves of Fig. 3-2 are at the intersections of the response surface with the equally spaced vertical planes $x_1 = 0$, 1, 2, 3, 4, and $x_2 = 0$, 1, 2, 3, 4.

By similar reasoning we can conclude that a point, which is at the simultaneous intersection of three surfaces, must be considered a zero-dimensional object, for it can have no degrees of freedom. The point **p** in Fig. 3-2 is at the intersection of the response surface with the two planar surfaces $x_1 = 3$ and $x_2 = 2$.

Figure 3-3 shows another way of depicting a response surface graphically. A front view of the surface as seen from the negative side of the x_1 axis is given in Fig. 3-3 (a). It shows the five space curves on the surface

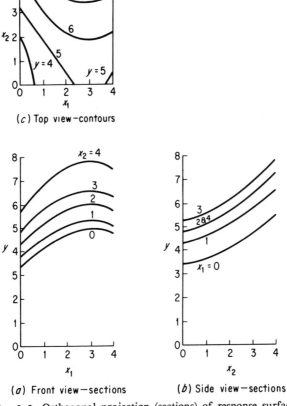

(c) Top view—contours

(a) Front view—sections   (b) Side view—sections

Fig. 3-3. Orthogonal projection (sections) of response surface.

for $x_2 = 0$, 1, 2, 3, and 4. Similarly the right side view in Fig. 3-3(b) consists of the projections of the space curves for $x_1 = 0$, 1, 2, 3, and 4 onto the y-x_2 plane, as they appear from the positive side of the x_2 axis. The curves shown in these views are the same as the ones in Fig. 3-2.

The curves in the top view, Fig. 3-3(c), are the projections onto the x_1-x_2 plane of intersections of the response surface with the horizontal planes on which $y = 3$, 4, 5, 6, and 7. These curves, known as *contours,* are also shown in the isometric projection of Fig. 3-4. In Fig. 3-3(c) these contours are all viewed from above. Readers who have studied mechanical drawing will recognize this technique of describing a solid object by three mutually perpendicular views as the method of *orthogonal projection.*

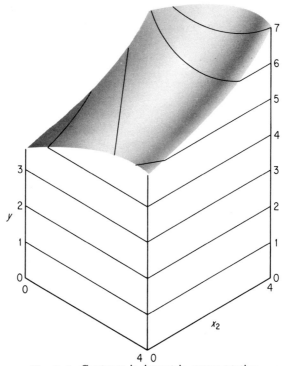

Fig. 3-4. Contours in isometric representation.

3.03. Hyperspace

Let us now generalize some of these geometric notions to situations where there are more than two independent variables. Suppose the criterion y is a function of n variables $x_1, x_2, \ldots, x_n$.

$$y = y(x, \ldots, x_n) \tag{3-2}$$

To represent this relation graphically one would need $n + 1$ axes all mutually perpendicular, which is physically impossible in our three-dimensional world. But even though we cannot construct such a coordinate system physically, we can certainly imagine a space of more than three dimensions if we are willing to extend the geometric concept of dimensionality by using the algebraic idea of degrees of freedom. It is customary to use the prefix *hyper-* to indicate any extension of ordinary solid geometry to spaces with more than three dimensions. Thus the term "$(n + 1)$-dimensional hyperspace" refers to the set of all possible points $(x_1, \ldots, x_n; y)$. In this terminology the set of points satisfying the single Eq. (3-2) would be an n-dimensional *hypersurface* imbedded in an $(n + 1)$-dimensional hyperspace. Similarly we may conceive of the intersection of the response hypersurface with any hyperplane on which y is constant as a *hypercontour*, an object of $n - 1$ dimensions. In the text to follow we shall be concerned with higher dimensional analogs of such geometric ideas as tangent and area, but we will not develop these more advanced concepts until we need them. All that we need to understand at the moment are the basic notions of space, dimension or degrees of freedom, and response surface.

The multivariable search problem can now be stated in geometric terms. It is desired to find the optimum (to be specific, say the maximum) value of some criterion y which depends on n independent variables x_1, $x_2, \ldots, x_n$. This function is unknown to us, but the value of y for any particular set of values of the $x_1, \ldots, x_n$ can be determined by experiment, as in Fig. 3-1, where the experiment conducted for $x_1 = 3$ and $x_2 = 2$ gives 5.9 for the value of y. Thus each point in the $x_1, x_2, \ldots, x_n$. hyperplane (where $y = 0$) corresponds to a possible experiment, the point above it on the response hypersurface representing the experimental outcome. Commonly the possible experimental points are confined to a bounded portion of the $x_1, \ldots, x_n$ hyperplane which will be called the *experimental region*. Each experiment gives us the elevation of the response surface above a new point in the experimental region. We wish to climb as high as possible on the response surface, using past information to guide the search for the summit.

3.04. Difficulties in multivariable search

At first glance one might think that the difference between multivariable search problems and the single variable ones already analyzed is only one of degree, that with a little extra calculation one could extend single variable methods to multivariable problems. Unfortunately this is not true, multivariable problems having a structure entirely different from that of a single variable one. Bellman[†] refers to the difficulties engendered by

[†] R. Bellman, *Dynamic Programming* (Princeton: Princeton University Press, 1957).

these differences as "the curse of dimensionality." This "curse" takes three forms in the problems of interest here.

One deleterious effect of multidimensionality is that it makes the unimodality assumption less plausible. To be sure, the definition of unimodality can be extended easily to the multidimensional case, but somehow it becomes more difficult to believe in unimodal response surfaces as the number of dimensions increases. However, as we shall see in our coming discussion of unimodality, there are enough examples of unimodal functions of several variables to justify their study here.

A more serious consequence is that we will be unable to find a measure of search effectiveness that does not depend on the experimenter's luck in some way. You will recall that the minimax methods developed for unimodal functions of a single variable gave the same length of final interval of uncertainty no matter where the peak happened to be. To see why the measures of effectiveness used previously are not valid in multidimensional problems, consider the two experiments $\mathbf{a} = (3, 2)$ and $\mathbf{b} = (1, 1)$ used to find, in the experimental region $0 \leq x_1 \leq 4$, $0 \leq x_2 \leq 4$, the maximum of the function given in Eq. (3-1). The values of y, respectively 5.9 and 4.6, are shown in Fig. 3-5. The function is unimodal above

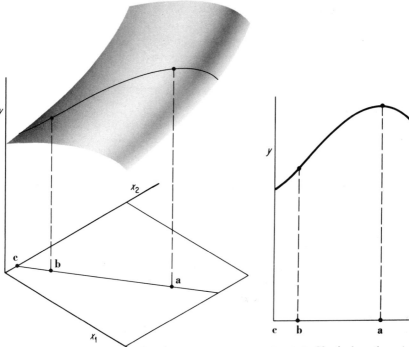

Fig. 3-5. Two experiments.

Fig. 3-6. Vertical section along line through **a** and **b**.

the straight line passing through **a** and **b**, as is verified in Fig. 3-6 which shows the curve at the intersection of the response surface with the vertical plane passing through **a** and **b**. Therefore we can conclude that the maximum sought cannot be above the line segment between **b** and **c**, the latter point being where the line intersects the boundary of the experimental region. Unfortunately, the line segment eliminated is negligible compared to the two-dimensional experimental region remaining. Thus multidimensionality overpowers the search techniques that were so effective when we only had lines to deal with.

The preceding analysis, which exposed the weakness of one-dimensional techniques in multidimensional experimental regions, suggests that areas be eliminated instead of line segments. This can and will be done, as we shall soon see. Thus it will be in fact possible for any particular search problem to use the areas of uncertainty remaining as a measure of search effectiveness. But we no longer will be able to predict in advance how large, or even what shape, the final region will be. Consequently there will be no objective way of comparing various methods in advance, and we shall be unable to exhibit a multidimensional search method which is in any way optimal.

The third difficulty is the very size of multidimensional spaces. This is a subtle point, difficult to visualize. To overcome our lack of multidimensional experience, let us attempt to imagine what happens to size as we pass from a one-dimensional line to a two-dimensional square and then to a three-dimensional cube.

Consider a line of unit length, the top edge of the cube in Fig. 3-7. Suppose we had a search method which would leave us with a final interval of uncertainty of 0.1, only one-tenth of the initial length. Such a technique would in effect select, from among ten equally sized segments of the line, the interval containing the optimum, and this interval looks relatively small compared to the original one of unit length.

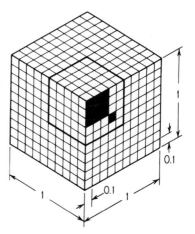

Fig. 3-7. The third curse of dimensionality.

Next imagine a unit square divided into squares each measuring 0.10 units on the side, as on one of the faces of the cube of Fig. 3-7. The darkened region shown comprises ten of these hundred squares—again, one-tenth of the original region. Somehow, this tenth of a square looks larger than the tenth of the line.

This effect is more marked in the unit cube of Fig. 3-7, which has been divided into one thousand cubes each measuring 0.10 unit on a side, To encompass ten per cent of this region we must take a hundred cubes, in Fig. 3-7 a volume measuring $0.4 \times 0.5 \times 0.5$. We see that a ten per cent interval of uncertainty, which looked small enough on a line, appears rather large on a cube. If we were dealing with a function of fifty variables the hyper-cube containing only ten per cent of the volume would measure $(0.1)^{1/50} = 0.93$ units on a side!

This phenomenon, which may appear paradoxical at first, arises from our application of a first degree measure, namely percentage, to a high degree quantity, namely volume and its multidimensional generalization. Thus even if we had a search method guaranteed to cut down the multi-dimensional volume of uncertainty to a fixed fraction, this percentage would have to be extremely small before the ranges of the individual independent variables would be significantly reduced. This difficulty, which might be called the "vastness" of hyperspace, has been pointed out by Hooke and Jeeves in a comment on the *random search* method of Brooks to be discussed next.[†]

Thus multidimensionality hurts us in three ways: it weakens our belief in unimodality, it takes away the *a priori* measure of effectiveness which lead to the powerful unidimensional minimax techniques, and it forces us to seek regions of uncertainty which are but tiny fractions of the original experimental region. But these obstacles, in making the quest for efficient search techniques more difficult, at the same time makes it more interesting. Research on the multidimensional search problem is really only beginning.

3.05. Random search

In the foregoing discussion of the "size" of multidimensional spaces, we divided a unit cube into 1000 cubical cells all measuring 0.1 unit on a side. Let us assign to each cell the average value that the criterion of effectiveness takes within it. Then we can rank the cells as best, second best, and so on. Suppose we wish to find one of the best hundred cells according to this ranking. These cells comprise the best ten per cent of the thousand cells.

If we choose a cell at random, then the probability that it will be one of the hundred best will be, of course, $\frac{100}{1000} = 0.1$. From another point of view, the probability of *not* selecting one of the best ten per cent on a single trial is $1 - 0.1 = 0.9$. If we select two cells at random, the probability of missing both times is $(0.9)^2 = 0.81$, which is naturally lower than for a

[†] R. Hooke, and T. A. Jeeves, "Comments on Brooks' Discussion of Random Methods," *Operations Research*, **6**, 6 (Nov. 1958), pp. 881-2.

single attempt. Thus the probability of finding at least one good cell in two tries increases to $1 - 0.81 = 0.19$. In general, after n cells have been chosen at random the probability $p(0.10)$ of finding at least one cell among the best 10 per cent is $p(0.10) = 1 - (0.9)^n$. After 16 trials this probability would be up to 0.80; 44 trials would give a probability of 0.99—almost a certainty. Notice that if the experimental region were unidimensional this interval of uncertainty of 0.1 would require 18 simultaneous trials or six sequential ones.

This random search procedure as proposed by Brooks[†] has two attractive features. First, no assumptions about the form of the response surface need be made—the method performs in the same manner on multimodal functions as on unimodal ones. Secondly, the probability $p(f)$ of finding at least one cell in the best fraction f of the experimental region does not depend on the number of dimensions, for, in generalization of the case already discussed,

$$p(f) = 1 - (1 - f)^n$$

or

$$n = \frac{\log (1 - p(f))}{\log (1 - f)}$$

Table 3-1, taken from Brooks' article, shows how f, $p(f)$, and n are related.

Table 3-1

NUMBER OF TRIALS REQUIRED IN A MAXIMUM-SEEKING EXPERIMENT
CONDUCTED BY THE RANDOM METHOD

f	$p(f)$			
	0.80	0.90	0.95	0.99
0.10	16	22	29	44
0.05	32	45	59	90
0.025	64	91	119	182
0.01	161	230	299	459
0.005	322	460	598	919

On the other hand, the random method is not without its disadvantages. It is inherently a simultaneous rather than a sequential method, and we have seen in Chap. 2 what a drawback this can be. Moreover, the vastness of multidimensional space tends to dilute the effectiveness of any method trying to cut the region of uncertainty to a fixed fraction of the experi-

[†] Samuel H. Brooks, "A Discussion of Random Methods for Seeking Maxima," *Operations Research*, **6**, 2 (Mar. 1958), pp. 244–51.

mental region. The comment of Hooke and Jeeves on this point was paraphrased in the section preceding.

Actually, Brooks' ideas are more general than we have indicated so far. It is not necessary to divide the experimental region into cells; one can merely choose points at random. Brooks has also suggested a sequential version of random search which he calls the *creeping random* method. This technique involves making an initial guess and taking measurements at random in the vicinity of this first estimate. It is important not to distribute the trials uniformly; one must tend to bunch them around the starting guess. Then the best of these random trials is made the center of a second random exploration of somewhat narrower extent. The process is then iterated. We cannot describe this idea precisely without going more deeply into probability theory than we would like in this elementary monograph, and we turn now to procedures which advance toward the optimum by measuring geometric properties of the response surface.

3.06. Multivariable strategy

The multidimensional search problem is to find, after only a few experiments, a set of operating conditions yielding a value of the criterion y which is close to the best attainable. From another point of view, the problem is to reach a specified minimum acceptable level of performance in as few trials as possible. Geometrically speaking, we would like to climb up the response surface as quickly as possible, even though the only information we have about the surface comes from the past experiments we have run.

Thus each experiment has two purposes, not only to attain a good value of the criterion, but also to give information useful for locating future experiments where desirable values of the criterion are likely to be found. Throughout the search we must continually be deciding to climb or to explore. If we expend all our experiments on exploration, we may learn where the peak is but have no experiments near it. On the other hand, it would seem short-sighted to try to reach the top without exploring at all, for one might well end up far from the peak through ignorance of the behavior of the function. A master search plan, or strategy, is called for that properly combines achievement with exploration.

The character of the strategies considered here will change as the search progresses. At the beginning when nothing at all is known about the function, we must explore in some small region, chosen at random, so that we might place our next experiments where the criterion is higher. In the middle of a search, after having left the very low regions behind, we try to climb as fast as possible, exploring only when strictly necessary to guide our successive jumps. Toward the end of the search, when we are finally near the top, extensive exploration may be needed to attain any increase in elevation, the slope of the response surface often being slight near the maximum. Another reason for surveying rather closely the region near a supposed maximum is to check whether it really is a maximum or not.

Thus, multidimensional search strategy, like chess strategy, seems to have three phases: opening game, middle game, and end game. The opening moves set the stage, the middle ones push for advantages, the final ones strive to reach the goal. We shall see that the various search schemes to be discussed differ from each other only in the middle phase, for each strategy will always begin and end with an exploration. This strategic approach, in which the experimenter changes tactics as the search moves on, seems to work well in practice according to some empirical studies of Lapidus, *et al.*[†] The first and last phases of search strategy will now be examined in turn, the more complicated middle strategies being deferred to Chap. 4.

OPENING GAMBIT

Let us begin the discussion of search strategy by studying the problem of locating the first few experiments. Since we have no advance information about the criterion function, the opening trials must be purely exploratory. We shall see that all they will tell us is our elevation on the response surface and which way we need move to go up from our initial group of experiments.

3.07. Linear exploration

To avoid being too abstract at the very beginning we shall consider the particular problem of finding the maximum, in the square experimental region $0 \leq x_1 \leq 4$, $0 \leq x_2 \leq 4$, of an unknown function $y(x_1, x_2)$ of two independent variables x_1 and x_2. Since nothing is known about the function $y(x_1, x_2)$, one point in the experimental region is as good a place to begin as any other, but for the sake of being specific let us start at the exact center, that is, at (2.0, 2.0). We shall call this initial point $\mathbf{x}_0$. Its first coordinate will be written x_{01}; its second, x_{02}. Thus

$$\mathbf{x}_0 = (x_{01}, x_{02})$$

and in this case $x_{01} = x_{02} = 2.0$. The outcome of the experiment $\mathbf{x}_0$ will be

† L. Lapidus, E. Shapiro, S. Shapiro, and R. E. Stillman, "Optimization of Process Performance," *A.I. Ch. E. J.* **7**, 2 (June 1961), pp. 288–94.

be denoted by y_0, and let us suppose that this result happens to be 5.70. The point $(x_{01}, x_{02}; y_0)$, which will be abbreviated $\mathbf{y}_0$, will be on the response surface directly above $\mathbf{x}_0$, as shown in Fig. 3-8.

Not much has been gained by this initial trial, for we still have no idea where to put the next experiment. Suppose, however, that we knew the general slope of the response surface in the neighborhood of the point $\mathbf{y}_0$. Then we would have at least a rough notion of which combination of changes in x_1 and x_2 might bring an increase in the criterion y. To find the slope in the direction parallel to the x_1 axis we need only run an experiment $\mathbf{x}_1 = (x_{11}, x_{12})$ whose second coordinate x_{12} is the same as for the initial trial. That is, we set

$$x_{12} = x_{02}$$

The first coordinate x_{11} should however be slightly different from x_{01}. In order to get an accurate estimate of the slope we must place $\mathbf{x}_1$ as close as possible to $\mathbf{x}_0$, allowing just enough distance between them to make the outcome y_1 distinguishable from y_0. Let us take, in this example,

$$\mathbf{x}_1 = (2.1, 2.0)$$

and suppose that the result is

$$y_1 = 5.72$$

then the situation after the first two experiments is that shown in Fig. 3-9. The straight line through the points $\mathbf{y}_0$ and $\mathbf{y}_1$ lies entirely in the vertical

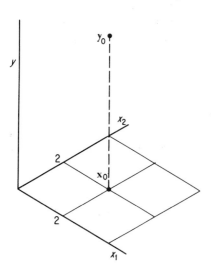

Fig. 3-8. Result of first experiment.

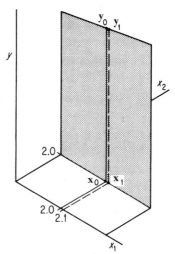

Fig. 3-9. Approximate tangent to response surface at $\mathbf{y}_0$ in plane $x_2 = 2.0$.

plane $x_2 = 2.0$ and is approximately tangent to the response surface at c_0. Its slope is given by

$$\left(\frac{\partial y}{\partial x_1}\right)_0 \approx \frac{y_1 - y_0}{x_{11} - x_{01}} = \frac{5.72 - 5.70}{2.1 - 2.0} = 0.2$$

where the subscript 0 indicates that the partial derivative is evaluated at the point y_0.

It would seem reasonable to locate the next experiment where x_1 is larger than at x_0 and x_1, since the criterion y seems to be increasing in this direction. One could indeed conduct a one-dimensional search to find the high point of the response surface in the plane $x_2 = 2$. From this high point we could then carry out another one-dimensional search in the x_2 direction, holding the co-ordinate x_1 at the value obtained on the previous search. This procedure could be continued, holding one variable constant and adjusting the other until the maximum is found. Unfortunately, as Box and Wilson have pointed out,[†] this method, described more fully in Chap. 4, will fail to find the maximum of a function shaped like the rising ridge of Fig. 3-10. The initial search along the line $x_2 = 2$ will find a summit at the point (3, 2) where the line crosses the ridge. Attempts to search for a higher point along the line $x_1 = 3$ would be doomed to failure, since (3, 2) itself is higher than any other point on that line. Therefore the search would terminate at (3, 2), far from the true maximum at (0, 4). The contours of this ridge are shown in Fig. 3-11.

It seems then that we should alter the x_2 coordinate at the same time as we change the coordinate for x_1. To decide whether x_2 should be increased

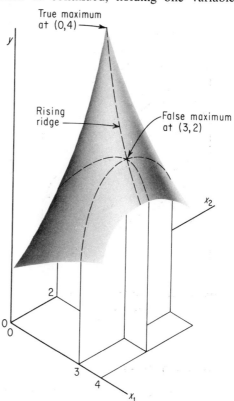

Fig. 3-10. Response surface with rising ridge—isometric view.

[†] G. E. P. Box and K. B. Wilson, "The Experimental Attainment of Optimal Conditions," *J. Roy. Stat. Soc.*, B13, 1 (1951).

or decreased we must perform another exploratory experiment very close to $\mathbf{x}_0$, this time varying the x_2 coordinate while holding the x_1 coordinate constant at x_{01}. Let us place an experiment at $(2.0, 1.9)$, to be designated $\mathbf{x}_2$. The decision to decrease the x_2 coordinate rather than to increase it for this exploratory run was, of course, completely arbitrary. If we suppose the outcome to be 5.67, then the situation after this third exploratory experiment will be as shown in Fig. 3-12. The straight line passing through points $\mathbf{y}_0$ and $\mathbf{y}_2$, approximately tangent to the response surface at $\mathbf{y}_0$, has a slope given by

$$\left(\frac{\partial y}{\partial x_2}\right)_0 \approx \frac{y_2 - y_0}{x_{22} - x_{02}} = \frac{5.67 - 5.70}{1.9 - 2.0} = 0.3$$

This tangent lies in the vertical plane $x_1 = 2.0$.

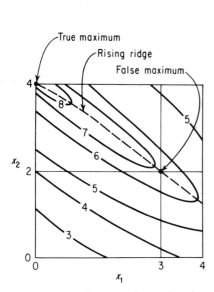

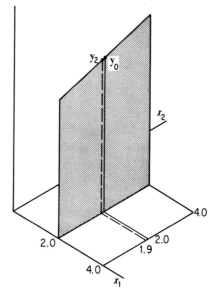

Fig. 3-11. Contours for surface in Fig. 3-9.

Fig. 3-12. Approximate tangent to response surface at $\mathbf{y}_0$ in plane $x_1 = 2.0$.

3.08. Tangent plane

We now know the slope of the response surface in two particular directions—parallel to the x_1 axis and parallel to the x_2 axis. What can we infer about the slope in other directions? The three points $\mathbf{y}_0$, $\mathbf{y}_1$, and $\mathbf{y}_2$ on the response surface are enough to determine the plane approximately tangent to the surface at $\mathbf{y}_0$. Let us find the equation of this tangent plane.

A plane in this three-dimensional space will satisfy an equation of the form

$$y(x_1, x_2) = m_0 + m_1 x_1 + m_2 x_2 \qquad (3\text{-}3)$$

where m_0, m_1, and m_2 are constants. Notice that since a plane has two degrees of freedom, it is a special kind of surface, as our geometric experience readily verifies. The particular character of a plane follows from the special form of Eq. (3-3), which expresses the criterion y as a *linear* function of the independent variables x_1 and x_2. By a *linear function* we mean a sum of terms, one a constant and each of the others a product of a constant and one of the variables raised to the first power. The word *linear* comes from the geometric fact that the intersection of two planes is a straight line. If any of the terms in Eq. (3-3) involved powers of x_1 and x_2 not equal to unity, or product of x_1 with x_2, then the equation would be *nonlinear* and the surface would be *curved*.

Knowing that the equation of the tangent plane must take the form of Eq. (3-3), we need only evaluate the three constants m_0, m_1, and m_2. One way to do this is to substitute into Eq. (3-3) the values of x_1, x_2, and y for the three exploratory experiments performed. This would give the following three independent equations in the three unknown coefficients m_0, m_1, and m_2.

$$y_0 = m_0 + m_1 x_{01} + m_2 x_{02} \qquad (3\text{-}4\text{a})$$
$$y_1 = m_0 + m_1 x_{11} + m_2 x_{12} \qquad (3\text{-}4\text{b})$$
$$y_2 = m_0 + m_1 x_{21} + m_2 x_{22} \qquad (3\text{-}4\text{c})$$

In the specific case under consideration, these equations would be

$$5.70 = m_0 + 2.0 m_1 + 2.0 m_2 \qquad (3\text{-}5\text{a})$$
$$5.72 = m_0 + 2.1 m_1 + 2.0 m_2 \qquad (3\text{-}5\text{b})$$
$$5.67 = m_0 + 2.0 m_1 + 1.9 m_2 \qquad (3\text{-}5\text{c})$$

It remains only to solve these equations simultaneously for m_0, m_1 and m_2.

In determining the equation of the tangent plane we shall find it convenient to deal only with the deviations of x_1, x_2 and y from the original point y_0. For the experiment $\mathbf{x}_i = (x_{i1}, x_{i2})$ let us define the deviations

$$\Delta x_{i1} = x_{i1} - x_{01} \qquad (3\text{-}6\text{a})$$
$$\Delta x_{i2} = x_{i2} - x_{02} \qquad (3\text{-}6\text{b})$$
$$\Delta y_i = y_i - y_0 \qquad (3\text{-}6\text{c})$$

In our example, $\Delta x_{i1} = x_{i1} - 2.0$, $\Delta x_{i2} = x_{i2} - 2.0$, and $\Delta y_i = y_i - 5.70$. This translation of co-ordinates eliminates the need to determine the intercept constant m_0, for by subtracting Eq. (3-4a) successively from Eqs. (3-4b) and (3-4c) and applying the Eqs. (3-6) we obtain

$$\Delta y_i = m_1 \Delta x_{i1} + m_2 \Delta x_{i2} \qquad \text{for } i = 1, 2 \qquad (3\text{-}7)$$

A further simplification results from the fact that x_1 was chosen to make $\Delta x_{12} = 0$ and that x_2 was chosen to make $\Delta x_{21} = 0$. For these special choices it is clear that

$$m_1 = \frac{\Delta y_1}{\Delta x_{11}} = 0.2 \approx \left(\frac{\partial y}{\partial x_1} \right)_0$$

$$m_2 = \frac{\Delta y_2}{\Delta x_{22}} = 0.3 \approx \left(\frac{\partial y}{\partial x_2} \right)_0$$

and therefore that the equation of the plane tangent to the response surface at y_0 is

$$\Delta y = 0.2\, \Delta x_1 + 0.3\, \Delta x_2 \qquad (3\text{-}8)$$

This tangent plane is shown in Fig. 3-13. The general equation of the plane, obtained by combining Eqs. (3-3) and (3-6), is

$$\Delta y = m_1\, \Delta x_1 + m_2\, \Delta x_2 \qquad (3\text{-}9)$$

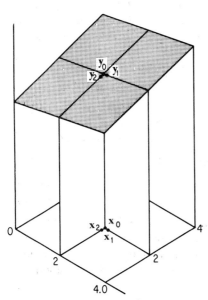

Fig. 3-13. Tangent plane at y_0.

Given Eq. (3-8) describing the tangent plane at y_0 we could, if we wished, estimate changes in y for any combination of small deviations in x_1 and x_2. For example, we would expect that value of y at (2.1, 2.1) to be about $5.70 + 0.2\,(0.1) + 0.3\,(0.1) = 5.75$. There is no reason then to make any further slope measurements, since no additional information would be gained. Hence, in accordance with our geometric intuition, only three experiments are needed to determine the tangent plane at y_0. Any three, not just the particular ones we chose, would have been acceptable as long as they did not all lie on the same straight line in the x_1-x_2 plane. The geometric reason for this restriction is that to determine a plane through a point one must have at least two different lines through the point. From an algebraic standpoint, three points on the same line would lead to Eqs. (3-7) that would not be linearly independent and which therefore could not give a unique solution for m_1 and m_2.

In order to guide our location of future experiments we shall be using the tangent plane as an approximate representation of the response surface in the neighborhood of y_0. It would be well at this point to examine the limitations on this approximation. Let us assume that the criterion function y is a continuous function of x_1 and x_2 with continuous first partial derivatives everywhere in the experimental region (this hypothesis will be weakened later on). Then we may expand y in a Taylor's series about the point y_0 as follows:

$$\Delta y = \left(\frac{\partial y}{\partial x_1}\right)_0 \Delta x_1 + \left(\frac{\partial y}{\partial x_2}\right)_0 \Delta x_2 + 0(x^2) \tag{3-10}$$

where $(\partial y/\partial x_i)_0$ is the partial derivative of y with respect to x_i, evaluated at the point y_0, and $0(x^2)$ represents terms of second order and higher. For sufficiently small deviations, these terms of higher order are negligible compared to the first order, or linear terms, which have precisely the same form as the tangent plane Eq. (3-9). Hence the coefficients m_1 and m_2 can be interpreted as approximations to the first derivatives $(\partial y/\partial x_1)_0$ and $(\partial y/\partial x_2)_0$ or conversely, the linear terms of Taylor's expansion can be considered to be the equation of the tangent plane at y_0. It follows that in the immediate vicinity of y_0 the tangent plane approximates very closely the behavior of the criterion y.

3.09. Contour tangent

When maximizing y we are interested only in combinations of Δx_1 and Δx_2 for which

$$\Delta y > 0 \tag{3-11}$$

Combining Eqs. (3-7) and (3-11) we obtain

$$m_1 \Delta x_1 + m_2 \Delta x_2 > 0 \tag{3-12}$$

which is the algebraic condition that a particular pair of deviations will produce an increase in y near y_0. In our example inequality, Eq. (3-12) becomes

$$0.2 \Delta x_1 + 0.3 \Delta x_2 > 0$$

This is the unshaded region of Fig. 3-14. The boundary of this region is, of course, the line $0.2 \Delta x_1 + 0.3 \Delta x_2 = 0$ passing through $(2.0, 2.0)$ whose slope in the x_1-x_2 plane is given by

$$\frac{dx_2}{dx_1} = \frac{\Delta x_2}{\Delta x_1} = -\frac{2}{3}$$

In geometric terms this line is simply the projection into the x_1-x_2 plane of the intersection of the tangent plane at y_0 with the contour plane $y = y_0$ (5.70 in this case; see Fig. 3-15).

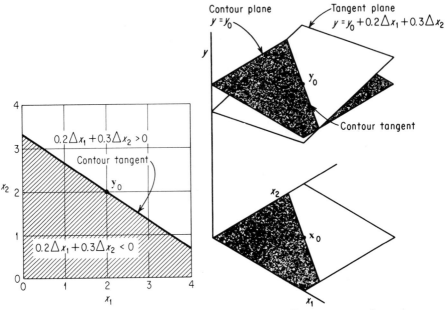

Fig. 3-14. Projection of contour tangent.   **Fig. 3-15.** Contour tangent in space.

From the information gained in three opening exploratory experiments we have found out which directions produce increases in y near y_0. All of the upward directions lie on one side of the line

$$m_1 \, \varDelta x_1 + m_2 \, \varDelta x_2 = 0 \qquad (3\text{-}13)$$

all of the downward directions being on the other. Although we now have a rough idea where to put the next experiment, which in order to attempt a significant increase in y should be quite some distance from y_0, we must leave precise decisions to the later sections concerning the middle game portion of the search strategy. We shall see that the linear approximations just developed, crude though they may seem, are common to all of the search methods to be considered.

Before leaving the subject of opening moves, we have two more ideas to discuss. The first involves the practicality of nonlinear, higher order local approximations, while the second is merely the generalization of the results already obtained to situations with more than two independent variables.

3.10. Nonlinear approximation

The linear approximation of Eq. (3-9) or (3-10) holds only for deviations Δx_1 and Δx_2 so small as to make second and higher order terms negligible in the Taylor expansion. One might wonder if it would be worthwhile to use some of these higher order nonlinear terms to obtain an approximation applicable over a somewhat larger region. The Taylor expansion, including the second-order terms, would be

$$\Delta y = \left(\frac{\partial y}{\partial x_1}\right)\Delta x_1 + \left(\frac{\partial y}{\partial x_2}\right)\Delta x_2 + \frac{1}{2}\left[\left(\frac{\partial^2 y}{\partial x_1^2}\right)(\Delta x_1)^2 + 2\left(\frac{\partial^2 y}{\partial x_1 \partial x_2}\right)(\Delta x_1)(\Delta x_2)\right.$$
$$\left. + \left(\frac{\partial^2 y}{\partial x_2^2}\right)(\Delta x_2)^2\right] + 0(\Delta x^3) \tag{3-14}$$

where all the derivatives are evaluated at y_0 and $0(\Delta x^3)$ represents terms of third and higher order in Δx. Abbreviating in an obvious fashion

$$m_{jk} = \left(\frac{\partial^2 y}{\partial x_j \partial x_k}\right)_0 \qquad j, k = 1, 2 \tag{3-15}$$

we obtain

$$\Delta y = m_1 \Delta x_1 + m_2 \Delta x_2 + \tfrac{1}{2}[m_{11}(\Delta x_1)^2 + 2m_{12}(\Delta x_1)(\Delta x_2)$$
$$+ m_{22}(\Delta x_2)^2] \tag{3-16}$$

in which there are five constants to be determined by experiment instead of the two in the linear case. This means that three additional experiments would be needed to fit a quadratic function to the response surface at y_0. A better use for these experiments would be to explore another point higher up on the response surface, since rarely would the local quadratic approximation have a range of validity much greater than that of the simpler linear approximation. There is little profit in exploring the vicinity near y_0 in great detail, since, having been chosen more or less at random, it is probably quite far from the maximum anyway. When we come to consider the last few experiments of the search, near the maximum, we shall turn to higher order approximations as suggested by Box and Wilson.[†] In the opening and middle phases, however, linear approximations would seem good enough.

3.11. Multidimensional generalization

Generalization of the results of this chapter to functions of many independent variables is quite easy using the algebraic concepts already developed. Let $y(x_1, x_2, \ldots, x_k)$ be a function of k independent variables,

† Box and Wilson, *op. cit.*

let $\mathbf{x_0} = (x_{01}, x_{02}, \ldots, x_{0k})$ be the original experiment, and let y_0 be its outcome. Define the deviations

$$\Delta x_j = x_j - x_{0j} \qquad \text{for } j = 1, 2, \ldots, k \qquad (3\text{-}17a)$$

$$\Delta y = y - y_0 \qquad\qquad (3\text{-}17b)$$

and let m_j be the derivative $(\partial y / \partial x_j)$ evaluated at $\mathbf{y_0}$. The linear approximation for y at $\mathbf{y_0}$ is

$$\Delta y = \sum_{j=1}^{k} m_j \, \Delta x_j \qquad (3\text{-}18)$$

To evaluate the coefficients m_j one must perform k experiments (not including $\mathbf{x_0}$) and solve the k simultaneous equations

$$\Delta y_i = \sum_{j=1}^{k} \Delta x_{ij} m_j \qquad \text{for } i = 1, 2, \ldots, k \qquad (3\text{-}19)$$

for the constants m_j, since the Δx_{ij} and Δy_i are given for each experiment. These computations can be simplified by choosing $\Delta x_{ij} = 0$ for all $i = j$, in which case Eq. (3-19) gives simply

$$m_i = \frac{\Delta y_i}{\Delta x_{ii}} \qquad \text{for } i = 1, 2, \ldots, k \qquad (3\text{-}20)$$

Once the m_j are known one can state that the combinations of Δx_j giving increased y near $\mathbf{y_0}$ must satisfy the inequality

$$\sum_{j=1}^{k} m_j \, \Delta x_j > 0 \qquad (3\text{-}21)$$

Geometrically speaking, if one considers the $k + 1$ dimensional space of y and the x_j, Eq. (3-18) describes the k dimensional hyperplane tangent to the response surface at $\mathbf{y_0}$. In terms of the experimental region, which is part of a space of k dimensions, the boundary between the upward region (that is, of increasing y) and the downward region is the $(n - 1)$-dimensional hyperplane satisfying the equation

$$\sum_{j=1}^{k} m_j \, \Delta x_j = 0 \qquad (3\text{-}22)$$

END GAME

With the study of opening moves completed it would seem natural to begin examining the middle game maneuvers which will bring us near the optimum sought. Instead we shall defer that topic to the next chapter and skip directly to discussing end game tactics because they have features in common with the opening gambits just described. Both the beginning and the end of a search involve local exploration, the former being a simple linear study near an arbitrary point and the latter, a nonlinear exploration of the vicinity of the optimum. Thus a fairly simple extension of the concepts already developed enable us to dispose of the end game tactics right now. Moreover, some of the geometric and algebraic ideas connected with nonlinear exploration will be of value later when we do discuss middle game tactics.

3.12. Nonlinear exploration

Box and Wilson[†] have remarked that often an experimenter is not satisfied merely with locating the optimum; he needs also know how the dependent variable behaves at points nearby. Since the tangent plane will be horizontal at a peak, curvature, asymmetry, and other nonlinear effects become important there, and the investigator is led to fit quadratic or higher degree expressions to the unknown function. Even an investigator totally unconcerned about the criterion's behavior near the summit would be reckless not to examine the supposed optimum rather closely, for there may actually be better points nearby. We shall study an example where the fitting of a quadratic expression signals the presence of higher ground which otherwise would have been overlooked.

First we measure the curvature by considering only the first and second degree terms of the Taylor expansion in the region of interest. If the function is quite asymmetric, cubic terms might be necessary, but we will find this out later when we check our quadratic predictions against actual observations. Box[‡] has discussed the dangers of trying to approximate a high degree expression with a lower degree polynomial. Since the work required to construct a nonlinear approximation grows rapidly with its degree, choice of a good algebraic representation for the function may well justify the initial research and reflection needed to obtain it, as pointed out in Chap. 1.

We shall develop the principles of non-linear exploration by studying a specific example. An investigator wishes to find the combination of temperature and chemical reactor volume for which the maximum profit, considering value of product less operating and construction costs, is obtainable. He has constructed a complicated mathematical model relating profit (y, \$/day) to the *logarithm* of temperature in degrees centigrade (x_1, dimensionless) and the reactor volume (x_2, cubic feet). The logarithm was chosen because theoretical considerations, namely, the Arrhenius

[†] Box and Wilson, *op. cit.*
[‡] G. E. P. Box, "The Exploration and Exploitation of Response Surfaces," *Biometrics*, **10** (1954), p. 16.

relation of chemical kinetics,[†] indicate that reaction rate is an exponential function of temperature. Use of the logarithm is more likely to give a representation which can be fit by a low degree polynomial.

Based on searching manuevers to be discussed in Chap. 4, the optimum appears to be near the point $(2.45, 8.5)$, where the profit is \$756/day, the highest measured. The daily profits at the four nearest points are as follows: $y(2.49, 8.5) = 574$; $y(2.45, 8.9) = 742$; $y(2.41, 8.5) = 646$; $y(2.45, 8.1) = 702$. In the experimental region obtained by plotting x_2 against x_1 the five points form a cross. As we shall see in Chap. 4, many search strategies give this sort of pattern in the neighborhood of a candidate for the optimum.

3.13. Noninteracting approximation

Equation (3-14) is the Taylor series for a function of two variables with the terms of higher than second degree neglected.

$$\Delta y = m_1 \, \Delta x_1 + m_2 \, \Delta x_2 + \tfrac{1}{2}[m_{11}(\Delta x_1)^2 + 2m_{12}(\Delta x_1)(\Delta x_2) + m_{22}(\Delta x_2)^2]$$
(3-14)

This expression has five constants, but there are available only four points different from the base point, which we shall take to be $(2.45, 8.5)$ in the center of the cross. We must either take another observation or throw out one term. As a first trial let us neglect the interaction term involving both Δx_1 and Δx_2. Thus we would have

$$\Delta y = m_1 \, \Delta x_1 + m_2 \, \Delta x_2 + \tfrac{1}{2}[m_{11}(\Delta x_1)^2 + m_{22}(\Delta x_2)^2] \qquad (3\text{-}23)$$

This approximation will be used to estimate the location of the true optimum. A check measurement there will tell us whether the approximation is good enough; if it isn't we shall use the check point to evaluate the constants when the interaction term is included.

The cross-like arrangement permits great simplification in the computations. Consider first the constants m_1 and m_{11} associated with the variable x_1. Let the base point $(2.45, 8.5)$ be designated $\mathbf{x}_0$; let the point $(2.49, 8.5)$ to its right be $\mathbf{x}_{11}$; and let $(2.41, 8.5)$ on the left be $\mathbf{x}_{12}$. With Δy_{ij} denoting $y(\mathbf{x}_{ij}) - y(\mathbf{x}_0)$ and Δx_{ij} being the distance from the base to the point $\mathbf{x}_{ij}$, we may write Eq. (3-23) for $\mathbf{x}_{11}$ and $\mathbf{x}_{12}$ as follows

$$\Delta y_{11} = m_1 \, \Delta x_{11} + \tfrac{1}{2}m_{11}(\Delta x_{11})^2 \qquad (3\text{-}24a)$$
$$\Delta y_{12} = m_1 \, \Delta x_{12} + \tfrac{1}{2}m_{11}(\Delta x_{12})^2 \qquad (3\text{-}24b)$$

But $\Delta x_{12} = -\, \Delta x_{11}$, and so the latter equation becomes

$$\Delta y_{12} = -\, m_1 \, \Delta x_{11} + \tfrac{1}{2}m_{11}(\Delta x_{11})^2 \qquad (3\text{-}24c)$$

† T. P. McCutcheon, H. Seltz, and J. C. Warner, *General Chemistry* (Princeton: D. Van Nostrand Co., Inc., 1939), p. 236.

Adding Eqs. (3-24a) and (3-24c) gives

$$m_{11} = \frac{\Delta y_{11} + \Delta y_{12}}{(\Delta x_{11})^2} \qquad (3\text{-}25\text{a})$$

Subtracting Eq. (3-24c) from Eq. (3-24a) gives

$$m_1 = \frac{\Delta y_{11} - \Delta y_{12}}{2\Delta x_{11}} \qquad (3\text{-}25\text{b})$$

In general if there are k independent variables arranged so that there are points x_{i1} and x_{i2} such that

$$x_{i1} = x_0 + \Delta x_{i1} e_i$$

and

$$x_{i2} = x_0 - \Delta x_{i1} e_i$$

where e_i is the ith unit vector,

then

$$m_{ii} = \frac{\Delta y_{i1} + \Delta y_{i2}}{(\Delta x_{i1})^2} \qquad (3\text{-}26\text{a})$$

and

$$m_i = \frac{\Delta y_{i1} - \Delta y_{i2}}{2\Delta x_{i1}} \qquad (3\text{-}26\text{b})$$

In the example at hand, the approximation Eq. (3-23) would be

$$\Delta y = -900\Delta x_1 + 50\,\Delta x_2 - 90{,}000(\Delta x_1)^2 - 200(\Delta x_2)^2 \qquad (3\text{-}27)$$

This quadratic expression may be differentiated partially with respect to Δx_1 and Δx_2, the derivatives set equal to zero, and the two equations solved simultaneously to give the coordinates Δx_1^* and Δx_2^* of the apparent optimum.
Thus

$$\frac{\partial \Delta y}{\partial \Delta x_1} = -900 - 180{,}000\Delta x_1 = 0$$

from which

$$\Delta x_1^* = -0.005$$

and similarly

$$\Delta x_2^* = 0.125$$

In general for this cruciform pattern

$$\Delta x_i^* = -\frac{m_i}{2m_{ii}} = \frac{(\Delta y_{i2} - \Delta y_{i1})\Delta x_{i1}}{\Delta y_{i2} + \Delta y_{i1}} \qquad (3\text{-}28)$$

Since the expression fit indicates that the optimum is indeed quite close to x_0, we might be tempted to conclude that the optimum has been found. It is prudent, however, to test another point first. Although the predicted optimum may seem like a good place to test, it is so close to the point x_0 that it would be of little value in subsequent surface fitting should the prediction be invalid. Thus we shall try the point (2.41, 8.9), obtained by *decreasing* x_1 an amount Δx_{11} and *increasing* x_2 by Δx_{21}. This puts the new point not only in the same quadrant as the predicted optimum, but also where it will make future computations convenient. Equation (3-27) forecasts that at the new point the profit will be \$636/day—\$120 less than at the best point so far. Evaluation of this point shows the profit to be only \$490/day, indicating that the variables are interacting so strongly that the simple model should not be used.

3.14. Interaction

Equation (3-23) having failed, we are forced to use Eq. (3-14) with its additional interaction term $m_{12}(\Delta x_1)(\Delta x_2)$. Fortunately the calculations are quite simple, for since the interaction term will still be zero in expressions such as Eq. (3-24), the Eqs. (3-25) for m_i and m_{ii} remain valid. In fact the numerical values of m_1, m_2, m_{11}, and m_{22} already computed will be unchanged in the new expression. To evaluate m_{12} we need merely write Eq. (3-14) for the new point x^{12}, substituting the values of the known constants.

$$\Delta y^{12} = -264 = -900(-0.14) + 50(0.4) - 90,000(0.14)^2$$
$$- 200(0.4)^2 + m_{12}(-0.04)(0.4)$$

whence $m_{12} = 9000$, clearly not negligible.

Before finding the optimum according to the new expression, let us indicate how to handle interaction when there are more than two independent variables. For k variables there will be $k(k-1)/2$ interaction terms each requiring a point. To evaluate the coefficient m_{ij}, place a new point at

$$x^{ij} \equiv x_0 \pm \Delta x_i e_i \pm \Delta x_j e_j$$

where the $\pm$ indicates that the sign is arbitrary. Equation (3-14), when written for this point, will have m_{ij} as its only unknown, since all the constants m_i and m_{ii} have already been determined.

Next we re-estimate the location of the optimum by differentiating Eq. (3-14), which in this case is now

$$\Delta y = 900\Delta x_1 + 50\Delta x_2 - 90,000(\Delta x_1)^2 + 9000(\Delta x_1)(\Delta x_2) - 200(\Delta x_2)^2$$
$$(3-29)$$

Solution of the two simultaneous equations resulting gives

$$\Delta x_1^* = -0.01$$

and

$$\Delta x_2^* = -0.10$$

A test at the corresponding point $\mathbf{x}^* = (2.44, 8.4)$ verifies the slight profit improvement of \$2/day predicted by Eq. (3-29). Hence we shift our co-ordinate system to put $\mathbf{x}^*$ at the origin, defining

$$\Delta \bar{x}_1 \equiv x_1 - x_1^* = \Delta x_1 + 0.01 \qquad (3\text{-}30a)$$
$$\Delta \bar{x}_2 \equiv x_2 - x_2^* = \Delta x_2 + 0.10 \qquad (3\text{-}30b)$$

To obtain a quadratic expression valid in the vicinity of this apparent optimum we could invoke Taylor's theorem, using Eq. (3-29) to give us the first and second derivatives we need. But we know already that at the optimum the first derivatives vanish, and the values of the second derivatives of a quadratic expression are necessarily the same no matter where they are evaluated. Therefore

$$\Delta \bar{y} \equiv y - y^* = y - 756$$
$$= -90,000(\Delta \bar{x}_1)^2 + 9000(\Delta \bar{x}_1)(\Delta \bar{x}_2) - 200(\Delta \bar{x}_2)^2 \qquad (3\text{-}31)$$

The right member is called a *homogeneous quadratic form* in two variables because each term is of second degree. For k independent variables a homogeneous quadratic form would be expressed by

$$\sum_{i=1}^{k} \sum_{j=1}^{k} \Delta \bar{x}_i m_{ij} \Delta \bar{x}_j$$

where the m_{ij} are known constants.

3.15. Peaks and saddles

If the point $\mathbf{x}^*$ is truly a maximum, and if the terms of third order and higher in the Taylor series are really negligible, then any combination of small changes $\Delta \bar{x}_1$ and $\Delta \bar{x}_2$ can only decrease the profit. In other words, $\Delta \bar{y}$ would always be negative for any choice of Δx_1 and Δx_2. Such a function, said to be *negative definite,* would have elliptical contours surrounding the peak as shown in Fig. 3-16(a). But it is well known that quadratic functions may also give hyperbolic contours such as those in Fig. 3-16(b), in which case $\mathbf{x}^*$ would not be a peak, but rather the summit of a pass, or saddle-shaped region, from which some directions lead up and some down. In algebraic terms, the quadratic form for a saddle-point would be *indefinite,* since some combination of $\Delta \bar{x}_1$ and $\Delta \bar{x}_2$ would make $\Delta \bar{y}$ negative while others would make it positive. Our present task then is to see whether Eq. (3-31) is definite or indefinite. And if it is indefinite, we want to find where the higher profits might be.

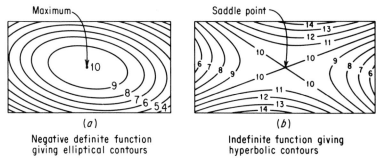

(a) Negative definite function giving elliptical contours

(b) Indefinite function giving hyperbolic contours

Fig. 3-16. Quadratic peak and saddle.

If either the sign of $(\Delta \bar{x}_1)^2$ or $(\Delta \bar{x}_2)^2$ were positive, then we would know immediately that $\Delta \bar{y}$ could be made positive by making the variable with the negative term equal to zero. Since this would also nullify the interaction term, any nonzero value of the other variable, when squared, would make $\Delta y > 0$. But this is not the case here, and so we must use more powerful methods.

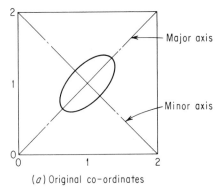

(a) Original co-ordinates

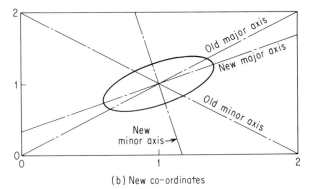

(b) New co-ordinates

Fig. 3-17. Distortion due to scale change.

There is a well-known, although computationally difficult, method for finding the axes of a quadratic form. This procedure, called *reducing the function to canonical form,* involves finding all the roots of an equation whose degree is equal to the number of independent variables. If all of the roots are negative, then the quadratic form is known to be negative definite; but any positive roots indicate indefiniteness. At first glance this procedure would seem attractive because with more computations (solution of k sets of simultaneous equations, each involving k equations in k unknowns) one can find the orientations of the axes of the quadratic form, which would help the investigator visualize the function. Unfortunately, every change of scale of any of the independent variables would distort the ellipses or hyperbolas, making a new reduction to canonical form necessary (see Fig. 3-17).

In ordinary Euclidean geometry the idea of canonical form is uniquely defined, but not in most physical problems where no concept of length can be defined objectively. Thus in our problem there would seem to be little advantage in putting the quadratic form in canonical form, since we have chosen the units of reactor volume arbitrarily anyway. The paradoxes arising from the fact that graphs of physical variables are usually non-Euclidean (no length defined) will be developed at more length in the next chapter. Readers interested in reduction to canonical form may wish to read about it in texts on algebra†, matrix theory‡, or experimental design.§

3.16. Completing the square

There is a method for finding whether a quadratic form is elliptic or hyperbolic which is not difficult to carry out and which also tells how to move away from a saddle point to improve the criterion. The procedure involves completing the square successively until the quadratic form is expressed as a sum of squared terms. Determination of the definiteness or indefiniteness is then simply a matter of inspection of the signs of the squared terms. If all are negative, the form must be negative definite.

In our example one of the squared terms is grouped with the interaction term. A multiple of the other squared variable is added to the first two terms so as to make the sum of the three terms a perfect square. To compensate for this addition, the same multiple is subtracted from the

† G. Birkhoff and S. MacLane, *A Survey of Modern Algebra* (New York: The Macmillan Company, 1953), pp. 275–78.

‡ R. A. Frazer, W. J. Duncan, and A. R. Collar, *Elementary Matrices* (Cambridge: Cambridge University Press, 1957), pp. 64–69.

§ O. L. Davies, ed., *The Design and Analysis of Industrial Experiments* (New York: Hafner Publishing Co., Inc., 1956), pp. 522–31.

existing squared term. Forms of two variables are immediately reduced to a sum of perfect squares by this procedure. In our example the transformation is

$$\Delta \bar{y} = -90{,}000(\Delta \bar{x}_1)^2 + 9000(\Delta \bar{x}_1)(\Delta \bar{x}_2) - 200(\Delta \bar{x}_2)^2$$
$$= -[90{,}000(\Delta \bar{x}_1)^2 - 9000(\Delta \bar{x}_1)(\Delta \bar{x}_2) + 225(\Delta \bar{x}_2)^2] + 25(\Delta \bar{x}_2)^2$$
$$= -(300\Delta \bar{x}_1 - 15\Delta \bar{x}_2)^2 + 25(\Delta \bar{x}_2)^2 \qquad (3\text{-}32)$$

This expression is indefinite because the two squared terms have different signs. Hence the point x^* is not a peak; it is a saddle. Notice that the expression would have been different if we had eliminated x_2 first. This does not matter because we are merely interested in the arrangement of signs, which is known as the *signature* of the function.

Since x^* is in reality a saddle, there is the possibility of further improvement of the profit. To do this we must choose a combination of $\Delta \bar{x}_1$ and $\Delta \bar{x}_2$ which will make Eq. (3-32) positive. Let us for the sake of convenience simply nullify the first term by taking

$$\Delta \bar{x}_2 = 20\Delta \bar{x}_1 \qquad (3\text{-}33)$$

Since the second term must always be positive, any pair of values satisfying Eq. (3-33) will be satisfactory; we shall choose $\Delta \bar{x}_1 = 0.02$ and $\Delta \bar{x}_2 = 0.4$. Equation (3-32) predicts $\Delta y = 4$ at this point and so if this value is verified we should search in this direction. Notice that if opposite signs were chosen the improvement would be the same, which indicates that there are two possible peaks to be examined.

If the experiments do not confirm the predictions of the equation, then the observer is forced to consider fitting a cubic equation, but we shall not go into this matter here. It is important to notice that the direction of improvement was found from data which at first glance would suggest that no better profit was possible. Directions of improvement can be found only if the interaction term is taken into account; the simpler no-interaction model is unsuitable because it involves only squared terms. Figure 3-18 shows the contours of the criterion function.

The process of completing the square can be carried out for any number of variables. Each iteration of the procedure gives a perfect square plus a remainder involving one less variable than before. For example, consider the reduction of the following three variable quadratic form.

$$x_1^2 + 5x_2^2 + 6x_3^2 - 4x_1x_2 + 2x_1x_3 - 8x_2x_3$$
$$= [(x_1^2 - 4x_1x_2 + 2x_1x_3) + (4x_2^2 + x_3^2 - 4x_2x_3)] + x_2^2 + 5x_3^2 - 4x_2x_3$$
$$= (x_1 - 2x_2 + x_3)^2 + (x_2^2 - 4x_2x_3 + 4x_3^2) + x_3^2$$
$$= (x_1 - 2x_2 + x_3)^2 + (x_2 - 2x_3)^2 + x_3^2$$

The method was to gather all of the terms containing x_1 and then complete

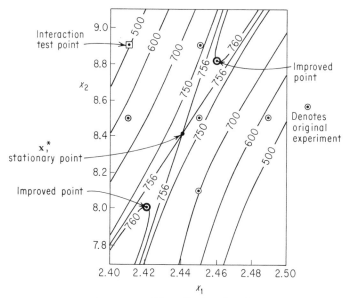

Fig. 3-18. The criterion function.

the square, leaving a remainder involving only x_2 and x_3. Next all the remaining terms containing x_2 were collected and the square completed again, leaving finally a remainder in x_3 only. This function is *positive definite* and indicates a minimum at the origin. The theoretical background for this technique is developed in Birkhoff and MacLane.[†]

3.17. Evolutionary operations

The optimum conditions may change slowly as time passes. Faced by this possibility, the experimenter would be wise to monitor the location of the optimum by continually checking the parameters of the nonlinear approximation fitted in the neighborhood of the optimum. Then any shift in the optimum will be picked up immediately.

In most large scale industrial operations any observations are obscured by appreciable experimental error. One must make many repeated measurements to distinguish between true changes in optimum conditions and the spurious fluctuations caused by random noise. Since experimentation with a full-size manufacturing plant is a costly business, monitoring of a moving optimum would be out of the question were it not for the large amount of data available for small changes in the independent variables. Hence if the experimenter is patient and uses good statistical techniques in gather-

[†] Birkhoff and MacLane, *op. cit.*, p. 269.

ing and analyzing his information, he may be able to make the plant slowly follow shifts in optimum conditions.

This idea of letting a system adapt to changing conditions without unduly upsetting it dynamically or sacrificing profits is due to G. E. P. Box[†], who named the procedure *evolutionary operations,* perhaps in the spirit of the Darwin Centennial being celebrated at that time. The book-keeping details of evolutionary operations are not within the scope of this book, which assumes no statistical background on the part of the reader. The method deserves attention, however, for it has proven itself valuable in industrial optimization. Its principles are very close to those we have described for fitting a nonlinear function to the response surface near the optimum.

GLOBAL PROPERTIES

All of the maximum-seeking strategies with which we are acquainted involve using data from local explorations to estimate where regions of higher response are likely to be and then placing new experiments in these promising regions. Thus if the hopeful predictions based on previous information are fulfilled, each new group of experiments will be higher on the response surface than the ones preceding it. Before describing the various search techniques in detail it is pertinent to ask under what conditions procedures of this type will always lead us to the summit.

To answer this question it will be necessary to consider such *global properties* of surfaces as unimodality and concavity, to be defined precisely later on. The term *global property,* borrowed from differential geometry,[‡] refers to any property which, being common to every point on a surface, can be considered characteristic of the entire surface. On the other hand, a *local property,* the slope of the tangent plane for example, can vary from point to point. The search procedures to be developed will involve proceeding from one group of local explorations to another, using measurements of the local tangents combined with known (or assumed) global properties to guide the search. For this reason a detailed description of certain important global properties is in order here.

3.18. Paths and Parametric representation

To discuss global properties precisely we must introduce the notion of a *path* in the experimental region. By a *path from point* **a** *to point* **b** *in*

[†] G. E. P. Box, "Evolutionary Operation: A Method for Increasing Industrial Productivity," *Appl. Statist.,* **6** (1957), pp. 81–101.

[‡] Dirk J. Struik, *Lectures on Classical Differential Geometry* (Reading, Mass.: Addison-Wesley Publishing Co., Inc., 1950).

the experimental region we shall mean any continuous curve whose end points are the points **a** and **b** and which lies entirely in the experimental region. Such a path may be considered as generated by a point moving from **a** to **b**. It may be helpful to picture this moving point as the center of successive sets of local explorations used during a search.

As an example, consider the path along the circular arc from the point $\mathbf{a} \equiv (2, 2)$ to the point $\mathbf{b} \equiv (1, 3)$ in Fig. 3-18. The equation of the circle, whose center is at $(1, 2)$, is

$$(x_1 - 1)^2 + (x_2 - 2)^2 = 1 \tag{3-30}$$

This curve has, of course, only one degree of freedom, there being two variables linked by Eq. (3-30). In order to suggest the generation of this curve by a point moving from **a** to **b** we shall express the coordinates x_1 and x_2 separately as functions of a single parameter θ which, as it runs through the range of its allowable values, traces out the arc from **a** to **b**. Consider the expressions

$$x_1 = 1 + \cos \theta \tag{3-31a}$$
$$x_1 = 2 + \sin \theta \tag{3-31b}$$

As θ varies from 0 to $\pi/2$ all of the points of the quarter circle are traced out by the generating point as it moves from **a**, where $\theta = 0$, to **b**, where $\theta = \pi/2$. The expression of each of the coordinates of a curve in terms of a single parameter is called the *parametric representation* of the curve.

Although parametric representation may seem artificial when there are only two independent variables, it is a natural way to describe curves in many dimensions. This is because a curve is a one-dimensional object whose single degree of freedom is clearly demonstrated in the parametric form, for as soon as one specifies a value of the parameter, one immediately knows all the co-ordinates of the point. Compare the simplicity of the parametric form to that involving $k - 1$ simultaneous equations relating the k independent variables. To find the coordinates of a point on the curve using the latter representation one would

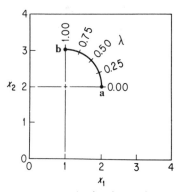

Fig. 3-19. A circular path.

have to specify one coordinate and then solve the $k - 1$ equations simultaneously to obtain the others, which would be a difficult and sometimes impossible computation problem. Another advantage of the parametric form is that it allows us to define direction of movement along the curve.

Thus the positive (negative) direction is merely the direction in which the parameter increases (decreases).

There are many different ways to express a curve in parametric form, but for the sake of simplicity we shall always use the *length* of the curve, as measured from the starting point **a**, as the parameter. To normalize the parameter λ we shall in fact define it as the distance (along the curve) from **a** divided by the total distance (along the curve) from **a** to the end point **b**. Thus the value of the parameter λ at a point will represent the fraction of the total length of the curve traversed up to the point in question. For the circular arc of Fig. 3-19, the length parameter λ should be $\theta\pi/2$, where θ was the angular parameter of Eq. (3-31). The parametric representation in terms of λ will then be

$$x_1 = 1 + \cos\frac{\lambda\pi}{2} \tag{3-32a}$$

$$x_2 = 2 + \sin\frac{\lambda\pi}{2} \tag{3-32b}$$

with $0 \le \lambda \le 1$. It is easily verified that λ is zero at **a** and unity at **b**.

Although we shall not be concerned here with the mechanics of expressing curves in parametric form, it will be instructive to exhibit the simple parametric representation of a straight line, and the result will be quite useful in the development to follow. Let **a** and **b** be two points in a space of n dimensions, and let **x** be any point on the straight line passing through **a** and **b** The coordinates of these points will be written

$$\mathbf{a} \equiv (a_1, a_2, \ldots, a_n) \tag{3-33a}$$
$$\mathbf{b} \equiv (b_1, b_2, \ldots, b_n) \tag{3-33b}$$
$$\mathbf{x} \equiv (x_1, x_2, \ldots, x_n) \tag{3-33c}$$

the parametric representation of the straight line through **a** and **b** is simply

$$x_j = a_j + (b_j - a_j)\lambda \quad \text{for all } j \tag{3-34}$$

This is equivalent to the vector equation

$$\mathbf{x} - \mathbf{a} = \lambda(\mathbf{b} - \mathbf{a}) \tag{3-35}$$

Notice that as λ runs from zero to unity **x** moves in a straight line, generating all points between **a** and **b**. Points beyond **b** are associated with values of λ greater than unity; similarly, $\lambda < 0$ for points outside the interval but closer to **a**. Figure 3-20 shows how λ varies along the line through the two points $(2, 2)$ and $(1, 3)$ in a plane.

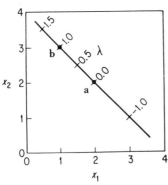

Fig. 3-20. A straightline path.

3.19. Unimodality

Now that we have defined a path and shown how to express movement along it, we are ready to study how the value of the y varies along a path. The criterion y is a function of the coordinates of the corresponding experiment $\mathbf{x}$, which in turn can all be expressed in terms of the parameter λ. That is,

$$y(x_1(\lambda), x_2(\lambda), \ldots, x_k(\lambda)) = y(\lambda) \tag{3-36}$$

along the path.

Since y depends only on the single parameter λ, we can borrow the concept of unimodality from the one-dimensional search theory developed in the preceding chapter. Let m represent the maximum value attained by y as λ passes through its range, and let λ^* designate the value of λ at which y equals m. That is,

$$m \equiv \max_{0 \leq \lambda \leq 1} y(\lambda) \tag{3-37}$$

and

$$y(\lambda^*) \equiv m \tag{3-38}$$

Let λ_i and λ_2 (with $\lambda_1 < \lambda_2$) be any two values of the parameter λ in the unit interval. Then we say that y is *unimodal on the path from* $\mathbf{a}$ *to* $\mathbf{b}$ if

$$\lambda_2 < \lambda^* \tag{3-39a}$$

implies that

$$y(\lambda_1) < y(\lambda_2) \tag{3-39b}$$

and if

$$\lambda^* < \lambda_1 \tag{3-40a}$$

implies that

$$y(\lambda_1) > y(\lambda_2) \tag{3-40b}$$

It is clear now how to define unimodality for a function of k variables. Let $\mathbf{x}^*$ be the point in the experimental region at which y reaches its maximum value y^*. That is,

$$y^* = \max_{\mathbf{x}} y(\mathbf{x}) \tag{3-41}$$

and

$$y(\mathbf{x}^*) \equiv y^* \tag{3-42}$$

Then the function $y(\mathbf{x})$ will be described as *unimodal* if for every pair of points $\mathbf{a}$ and $\mathbf{b}$ in the experimental region there exists a path from $\mathbf{a}$ through $\mathbf{x}^*$ to $\mathbf{b}$ on which y is unimodal.

This definition can be stated more simply by introducing the idea of a *strictly rising path*. For some path let λ_1 and λ_2 be any two values of the parameter λ in the unit interval. The path is said to be *strictly rising* if

$$\lambda_1 < \lambda_2 \tag{3-43a}$$

implies that

$$y(\lambda_1) < y(\lambda_2) \tag{3-43b}$$

Then a function $y(\mathbf{x})$ is *unimodal* if for every point $\mathbf{a}$ in the experimental region there exists a strictly rising path to the maximum at $\mathbf{x}^*$. This second definition is equivalent to the first. The surface whose contours are exhibited in Fig. 3-21(a) is unimodal; the one in Fig. 3-21(b) is not.

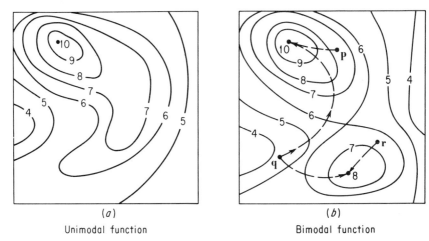

(a)   (b)

Unimodal function   Bimodal function

Fig. 3-21. Contours of two response surfaces.

It is not difficult to see that any search method which keeps to strictly rising paths must eventually reach the top of a unimodal function, even one as twisted as that shown in Fig. 3-21(a). On the other hand, one cannot be sure of success with such methods when the function has more than one peak as in Fig. 3-21(b). On this *bimodal* (doubly peaked) function the behavior of a strictly rising search technique depends on where the search starts. A search commencing above the saddle will end at whichever peak is inside the same loop of the saddle contour for $y = 6$. Thus a search at $\mathbf{p}$ will find the higher peak while one commencing at $\mathbf{r}$ can only converge to the lower one. A search starting below $y = 6$ may converge to either peak, depending on where the search first crosses the contour for $y = 6$. Such a point is $\mathbf{q}$ in Fig. 3-21(b), from which two rising paths have been drawn, one to the higher peak and one to the lower.

The definition of unimodality just developed is broad enough to include any function with a single peak, no matter how crooked its ridges and

valleys might be. It is not often, however, that the criteria being maximized is even as badly behaved as the function shown in Fig. 3-21(a).
In practice one would expect instead to encounter relatively smooth functions similar to the one shown in Fig. 3-22(a). One of the search techniques to be developed will turn out to be applicable to these smooth
functions but not to all unimodal functions, and to anticipate this future
discussion we shall construct now a formal definition describing these
special functions.

3.20. Strong unimodality

A function will be called *strongly unimodal* if the straight line running
to the summit at x^* from *any* point **a** in the experimental region is a
rising path. Figure 3-22 shows three *strongly* unimodal functions. Functions
with oval contours, such as the ones in Fig. 3-22(b) and (c) occur rather
often in practice; for example, the free energy function for a system of
reacting chemicals falls into this group. Many-ridged functions like that
shown in Fig. 3-22(a) are also *strongly* unimodal, although one would
expect such a function to be a rarity. For this reason it will be convenient
to define a more restricted class of functions that excludes this latter
group. A function will be called *linearly unimodal* if it is unimodal along
any straight line in the experimental region (not just those through the
summit).

A final still more restricted class of functions to be defined are the
ones that are *concave down*. Such a function is concave down along any
straight line in the experimental region, which means that for any two
points **a** and **b**, the function $y(x)$ obeys

$$y[a + \lambda(b - a)] \le y(a) + \lambda[y(b) - y(a)] \qquad (3\text{-}34)$$

where λ is the parameter of the straight line between **a** and **b**. The function
in Figure 3-22(c) is concave down; compare it with the ones in Figs.

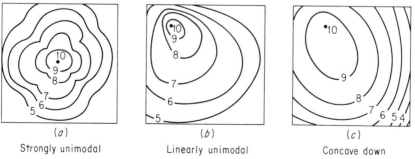

| (a) | (b) | (c) |
| Strongly unimodal | Linearly unimodal | Concave down |

Fig. 3-22. Strongly unimodal functions.

3-22(a) and (b), which are not. Any function which is concave down is strongly (and, of course, linearly) unimodal.

In this chapter we have discussed certain geometric properties of surfaces which will be useful in the development of search techniques to follow. Along the way we introduced the concept of a path in the experimental region and demonstrated the usefulness of the parametric description of curves in space. We are ready now to study the multidimensional search techniques themselves.

EXERCISES

1. Draw an isometric projection and the three orthogonal views for the following functions in the region $-2 \leq x_1 \leq 2$, $-2 \leq x_2 \leq 2$. Indicate all the maxima, minima, and saddles in the region
   (a) $y = x_1 x_2$
   (b) $y = x_1^2 + x_2^2 + x_3^2$
   (c) $y = \exp(-x_1^2 + x_2^2)$
   (d) $y = \ln(x_1^2 + x_1 x_2 - 2x_2^2)$
   (e) $y = x_1^3 + x_2^3$
   (f) $y = x_1^2 x_2^2$

2. Find the equation of the contour tangent through the point $(1, -2, 3)$ for the functions
   (a) $y = x_1^2 + x_2^2 + x_3^2$
   (b) $y = \exp[x_1^2 + x_3^2 - x_1 + 3x_2 + 2]$
   (c) $y = \ln(x_1^2 + x_1 x_2 + x_2^2)$
   (d) $y = x_1^3 + x_2^3$

3. Find the equation of the contour tangent through the point $(-2, 1, -1, 4)$, using the following data:

x_1	x_2	x_3	x_4	y
-2	1	-1	4	10.0
-1.9	1	-1	4	10.3
-2	1.1	-1	4	9.8
-2	1	-0.9	4	9.7
-2	1	-1	4.1	10.4

4. Estimate the value of y in the previous problem at the point
   $$(-1.5, 0.5, -0.5, 4.5).$$

5. Find the equation of the contour tangent through the point $(3, 4)$, using the following data:

x_1	x_2	y
3	4	6.4
3.2	4.2	6.8
2.8	4.1	6.3

6. Find the equation of the contour tangent through the point $(-2, 5)$, using the following data:

x_1	x_2	y
-2	5	11.5
-1.8	5.4	11.8
-2.2	4.6	11.2

7. Construct a quadratic approximation to the function $y = \exp[2x_1^2 + 2x_2^2 + x_1 - 5x_2 + 10]$ in the vicinity of $(0, 1)$. Where does the approximation predict the minimum to be? Compare the predicted value at this point with the actual value.

8. From the data given below, construct both a non-interacting and an interacting quadratic approximation. Compare the stationary points predicted by these approximations. Is the stationary point a maximum, minimum, or saddle?

x_1	x_2	y
1.0	4.0	5.85
1.0	3.0	5.85
1.0	2.0	6.00
2.0	4.0	6.10
2.0	3.0	6.10
2.0	2.0	6.10
3.0	4.0	5.85
3.0	3.0	6.05

9. Are the following forms definite or indefinite?
   (a) $x_1^2 - x_1x_2 + x_2^2$
   (b) $x_1^2 - 4x_1x_2 + x_2^2$
   (c) $4x_1^2 + 2x_2^2 + 9x_3^2 - 4x_1x_2 + 12x_1x_3 + 8x_2x_3$
   (d) $x_1^4 - 4x_1^2x_2^2 + 5x_2^4$
   (e) $x_1^3 - 4x_1^2x_2 + x_1x_2^2$

10. Indicate if the following functions are unimodal, strongly unimodal, linearly unimodal, concave up or down, or none of these in the region $0 \le x_1 \le 2$, $0 \le x_2 \le 2$.

   (a) $x_1^2 + x_2^2$
   (b) $\exp(-x_1^2 - x_2^2)$
   (c) $x_1^2 - x_2^2$
   (d) $x_1^2x_2^2$

Tangents
and Gradients

4

"O stay," the maiden said, *"and rest
Thy weary head upon this breast!"*
*A tear stood in his bright blue eye,
But still he answered with a sigh,
Excelsior !*
—*Longfellow*

After each local exploration has been made, one must decide where to look for further improvement in the criterion of effectiveness. This chapter will describe two basic middle game strategies for guiding the large steps from one local exploration to another. The strategies use the most recently determined linear approximation (geometrically, the tangent plane) to direct the next jump. These techniques tend to complement each other and could be used in combination.

First to be discussed will be the *contour tangent elimination* methods, so called because they use each locally measured tangent to the contour as a boundary eliminating part of the experimental region from further consideration. In this way they resemble the sequential search methods of Chap. 2 which involved successively reducing the size of an interval of uncertainty. Tangent elimination methods are the only multidimensional techniques whose effectiveness can be measured in terms of the size of the region of uncertainty remaining. But their effectiveness deteriorates rapidly in the face of experimental error, they can only be used on strongly unimodal functions, and their computations become cumbersome as the number of variables increases.

Gradient, or *steepest ascent* methods, will be developed also. These techniques point the new search in the direction perpendicular to the most recently determined contour tangent because in certain carefully restricted situations this *gradient direction* gives the greatest rate of change of the criterion per size of step. Unlike the contour tangent methods, the gradient methods can be used on any unimodal function even in the presence of large experimental error. But in many practical situations the gradient methods require a somewhat arbitrary decision concerning the scales for measuring the independent variables. This arbitrariness inhibits the usefulness of these techniques for reasons which, being rather subtle and not at all easy to understand, must be developed at some length. Gradient methods tend to oscillate, but we shall see in Chap. 5 how to take care of this characteristic.

CONTOUR TANGENT ELIMINATION[†]

Our description of middle game strategy begins with a discussion of *contour tangent elimination* methods, which use contour tangents (to be explained in the next paragraph) determined by successive local explorations of strongly unimodal response surfaces to eliminate parts of the experimental region from all further consideration. Since these methods use information from all past local explorations, they are able to reduce the region of uncertainty fairly rapidly. Their efficiency is, however, undermined by experimental error, which reduces the precision with which the contour tangents can be measured.

Let us begin by defining the contour tangent, both geometrically and algebraically. In Fig. 4-1, the point **a** lies on the contour $y = 6$, and the line tangent to this contour at **a** is called the *contour tangent*. The equation for the contour tangent is determined by noting that along the contour the criterion does not change, and so

$$\Delta y \equiv 0$$

For small changes Δy_i in the independent variables x_i, the changes Δy is given by the linear approximation of Eq. (3-18). Thus the equation of the contour tangent at **a** is Eq. (3-22),

$$\Delta y = \sum_i m_i \, \Delta x_i = 0$$

where the m_i are experimentally determined constants. When there are two independent variables, the contour tangent is a line in the two-dimensional experimental region, as shown in Fig. 4-1. In general the n-dimensional experimental region generated by n independent variables will be divided into two subregions by the contour tangent, an $(n - 1)$-dimensional hyperplane in this general case.

[†] D. J. Wilde, "Optimization by the Method of Contour Tangents," *Am. Inst. Chem. Engrs. Journ.* **9**, 2 (March 1963) pp. 186–90.

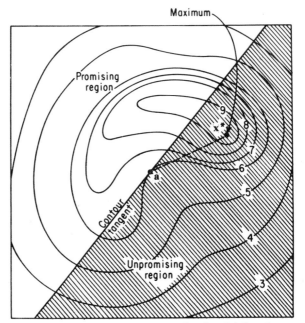

Fig. 4-1. Inapplicability to general unimodal function.

4.01. Elimination

As we pointed out earlier, the contour tangent at **a** forms the boundary between the upward region where the tangent plane at **a** lies above $y(\mathbf{a})$, and the downward region where the opposite is true. There are unimodal functions, such as that shown in Fig. 4-1, whose maximum $\mathbf{x}^*$ could be in the downward region. If, however, we restrict ourselves to *strongly* unimodal functions as in Fig. 4-2 then it would be impossible for the maximum $\mathbf{x}^*$ to be in the downward region. In this case we could confine our future explorations to the promising upward region.

Let us prove now that the maximum $\mathbf{x}^*$ of a strongly unimodal function cannot lie on the low side of any contour tangent, that is,

$$\sum_i m_i(x_i^* - a_i) \geq 0 \qquad (4\text{-}1)$$

where x_i^* and a_i are the ith components of the points $\mathbf{x}^*$ and **a**. This fact can be proven by assuming the contrary and forcing a contradiction. Suppose that, contrary to our assertion, the maximum $\mathbf{x}^*$ were on the low side of a contour tangent

$$\sum_i m_i(x_i^* - a_i) < 0 \qquad (4\text{-}2)$$

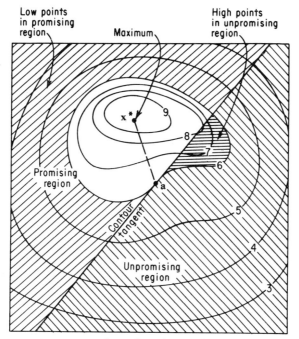

Fig. 4-2. Strongly unimodal function.

Let **x** be any point on the straight line between **a** and **x***. The parametric representation of **x** is

$$x_i - a_i = \lambda(x_i^* - a_i) \qquad \text{for all } i$$

where λ is a parameter ranging from 0 to 1

$$0 \le \lambda \le 1$$

If **x** is sufficiently close to **a**, that is, if λ is small enough (but not zero), then the value $y(\mathbf{x})$ of the criterion at **x** is given by Eq. (3-18), which in this context is

$$y(\mathbf{x}) - y(\mathbf{a}) = \sum_i m_i(x_i - a_i)$$

Since we have taken λ to be positive, we may write

$$y(\mathbf{x}) - y(\mathbf{a}) = \frac{1}{\lambda} \sum_i m_i(x_i^* - a_i)$$

whence, by the hypothesis (4-2),

$$y(\mathbf{x}) < y(\mathbf{a})$$

But this would mean that the criterion is not unimodal along the straight line between **a** and **x**, which contradicts our assumption that y is strongly unimodal. This contradiction arises from Eq. (4-2) which therefore must have been false. Thus the maximum x^* of a strongly unimodal function cannot be on the low side of any contour tangent.

It follows that we need not hesitate to eliminate the entire unpromising downward region from further consideration. This discarding of an entire region on the basis of one local exploration is so remarkable that one might at first suspect that we are perpetrating a clandestine and unwarranted extrapolation. Notice, however, that the elimination is justified not by extrapolating, but rather by invoking the global property of strong unimodality. As Fig. 4-2 shows, the unpromising region may contain places where the response is higher than at **a**, just as there may be portions of the desirable region which really give lower responses than at **a**. But this is not pertinent, for the contour tangent elimination is based on shooting for the *optimal* response, even though the quest fall occasionally into low response areas. Presently we shall suggest how to rise rapidly out of such areas where the criterion is low, but first we shall discuss the placement of the next block of experiments in the new, smaller experimental region.

4.02. Location of a new block

After cutting down the size of the experimental region, one must decide where to place the next block of experiments to determine another contour tangent. Clearly the next block should be somewhere inside the eligible region so that the new contour tangent will be certain to reduce the size of the experimental region even further. If successive local explorations are always made at interior points, the region of uncertainty eventually can be made as small as desired. This fact, together with the assumed unimodality of the criterion, guarantees that the maximum x^* can be approached as closely as the experimenter wishes, if he has enough experiments at his disposal.

Comforting as it is to know that any search sequence using interior points will in the long run attain the maximum, we are usually more interested in getting high values of the response y as soon as possible. Knowing nothing about y aside from its strong unimodality, we cannot use past values of y to guide the search. But we do know something about the independent variables x_i—the shape of the region of uncertainty remaining to be explored. Hence we can either attempt to get as close as possible to the maximum x^* or else try to make the region of uncertainty as small as we can. Either way we are led to locate each new block somewhere in the middle of the remaining region of uncertainty, for a point on the boundary risks either being quite far from x^* or giving a contour tangent with which only a tiny region can be eliminated.

Let us illustrate the block location problem with an example. Figure 4-3 shows yield from a chemical reactor as a function of operating temperature and pressure. The response surface is strongly unimodal. Notice that the contours are not necessarily oval and are in fact rather complicated. It is assumed that the experimenter knows nothing about the response surface except that the peak lies somewhere between 400°F and 600°F and between four and nine atmospheres. Experimental error is neglected, which would be reasonable in the study of a mathematical model too complicated to be optimized by such direct methods as the calculus.

The first block of experiments, denoted in Fig. 4-3 by the circled numeral 1, is located in the center of the original rectangular experimental region. The block consists of enough experiments (at least one more than the number of independent variables—three in this case) to determine the equation of the contour tangent in the vicinity of the block. This tangent, together with the region it eliminates, is shown in Fig. 4-3. The trapezoidal area remaining is, of course, only half as large as that of the original rectangle.

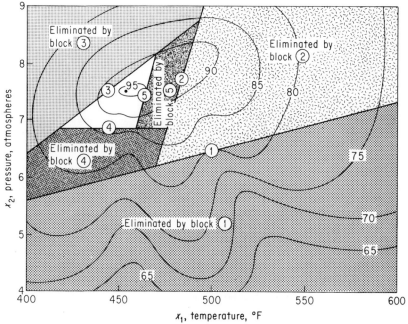

Fig. 4-3. Contour tangent elimination.

The second block is located at the "center of volume" of the trapezoid, where a new contour tangent is determined. Location of the center of volume, as well as three other possible center points, will be described in the sections following. For the moment it is only necessary to notice that again approximately half of the remaining region has been eliminated, leaving only about a quarter of the original area. In this example the procedure is continued until five blocks (at least fifteen experiments) are used. Since each block reduces the area of uncertainty by a factor of approximately two, one would expect the final area to be about one thirty-second (3.1 per cent) of that of the original region. The final region actually remaining is 3.2 per cent of the original, even though the contour tangents lie at many different angles.

Notice that blocks 4 and 5 give yields less than that at block 3. This is not surprising, because we have placed the blocks so as to cut down the region of uncertainty as rapidly as possible, not at all taking account of the yields obtained. As we shall show later, it is possible, at the cost of a few extra experiments, to have each block give a yield at least as good as that obtained in previous blocks while still reducing the region of uncertainty in an effective manner. We turn now to the details of locating successive blocks in the "middle" of the experimental region.

But exactly where is the "middle" of a region? This question is more easily asked than answered, and we shall in fact propose four different points as candidates for the middle. Before condemning us as hopelessly indecisive, permit us to remark that one has the same difficulty in choosing a measure of central tendency of a statistical distribution function, and in any particular case an experimenter might use either the mean, the mode, or the median, depending on his judgment and facilities for performing the required calculations. Similarly we must leave the choice of a middle point in a particular exploration entirely to the reader, although we will develop the advantages and disadvantages of each possibility to furnish a foundation for an intelligent decision.

The four points will be called respectively the *midpoint* $\mathbf{x}^{\cdot}$, the *minimax point* $\mathbf{x}^m$, the *center of volume* or *median* $\hat{\mathbf{x}}$, and the *centroid* or *mean* $\bar{\mathbf{x}}$. In the special case where the region of uncertainty is rectangular the four points will coincide. None of their locations are affected by the scales chosen to measure the independent variables, a property which we shall appreciate more fully when we study steepest ascent methods. Whenever the experimental region is convex, that is, such that any straight line connecting two boundary points will lie entirely within the region, any of the four points will be inside the region. Since any region bounded entirely by hyperplanes is convex, the region of uncertainty will tend to be convex after a few blocks of experiments have been performed. And even when the region is not convex, in practice the four points more often than not will be in the interior of the region. While each of them can be considered optimal according to some measure of search effectiveness, none of them can claim to be uncontestably best. Our discussion will therefore be limited to their definitions, justifications, and disadvantages.

4.03. Midpoint

The midpoint $x^{\cdot}$, by far the most easy of the four points to calculate, is at the same time based on the most cautious measure of effectiveness. As shown in Fig. 4-4, let s_i and t_i respectively be the minimum and maximum values assumed by the variable x_i in the region of uncertainty

$$s_i = \min x_i$$

and

$$t_i = \max x_i$$

The distances from any point x in the region to those limits, measured parallel to the respective x_i axes, are $(x_i - s_i)$ and $(t_i - x_i)$. Notice

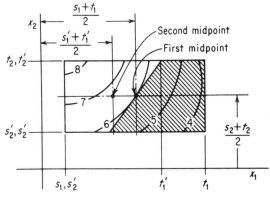

(a) Typical situation

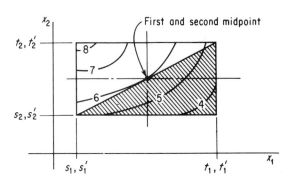

(b) Worst situation — no change

Fig. 4-4. The midpoint.

that we measure distances only in directions parallel to the axes, since as we shall point out later, such distances can be defined without fixing the scales of measurement, which we wish to avoid.

The next block of experiments will produce a new region with extremes s'_i and t'_i for which

$$s'_i \geq s_i$$

and

$$t'_i \geq t_i$$

In the worst possible circumstances, as in Fig. 4-4(b), these inequalities will be satisfied exactly and there will be no change in the extremes, although of course the new region itself will necessarily be smaller. Thus the distance $d(x_i)$ to the furthest extreme which could possibly remain would be

$$d(x_i) = \max\{(x_i - s_i), (t_i - x_i)\}$$

A conservative policy would be to locate the new block at the point $\mathbf{x}^*$ where this quantity would be *minimum* for every x_i. That is, we want to choose the components x^*_i of $\mathbf{x}^*$ such that

$$d(x^*_i) = \min_{s_i \leq x_i \leq t_i} d(x_i)$$

This point is clearly the one that is half way between the extremes. That is, for all i,

$$x^*_i = \frac{(s_i + t_i)}{2} \tag{4-3}$$

which is why we call $\mathbf{x}^*$ the *midpoint* of the region.

The midpoint is quite easy to calculate and seems to us a reasonable place to locate the next block when the region has no long protuberances. It is, however, perhaps too middle-of-the-road, being unduly influenced by the extreme points and not at all by points in the center of the region. While the midpoint is invariant under changes of scale, it will in general move if the coordinate system is rotated. Even though rotations are not well defined unless the variables all have the same dimensions, the sensitivity of the midpoint to rotations is unsatisfying, if only from an aesthetic viewpoint.

4.04. Minimax

Suppose that instead of ignoring all but the extreme points, as we did in the preceding analysis, we consider all points to be of equal importance regardless of their location. Then we would want the hypervolume (in two dimensions, the area) of the region of uncertainty remaining after the next block of experiments to be small as possible. To make this idea precise let $\mathbf{x}$ be a typical interior point, and let an arbitrary hyperplane (in two dimensions, a line) through this point be described by the equation

$$\sum m_i \, \Delta x_i = 0$$

where the deviations Δx_i are as usual measured from $\mathbf{x}$. This hyperplane will divide the region of uncertainty into two subregions whose respective hypervolumes will depend on the location of x_i and on the constants m_i. Let these two hypervolumes be represented by $v_1(\mathbf{x}, m_i)$ and $v_2(\mathbf{x}, m_i)$ with

$$v_1(\mathbf{x}, m_i) \leq v_2(\mathbf{x}, m_i)$$

Now although we can choose $\mathbf{x}$ at will, we have no way of predicting the orientation of the contour tangent hyperplane as indicated by the coefficients m_i. Neither can we say in advance whether the search will have to be continued in the larger or in the smaller subregion. Hence to be safe we must consider the worst conditions possible, under which the new region of uncertainty will have a hypervolume $v(\mathbf{x})$ given by

$$v(\mathbf{x}) = \max_{m_i} \{v_2(\mathbf{x}, m_i)\}$$

Let us locate the next block at the *minimax point* $\mathbf{x}^m$, where the largest possible hypervolume is as small as possible.

$$v(\mathbf{x}^m) = \min_{\mathbf{x}} \{v(\mathbf{x})\} \tag{4-4}$$

The minimax point has several desirable theoretical characteristics. It is insensitive not only to scale changes, but, unlike the midpoint $\mathbf{x}^{\cdot}$, to rotations of the axes as well. Furthermore, it is possible in principle to predict with certainty just what the largest possible hypervolume remaining would be after a given number of blocks located at successive minimax points. This remainder would be an *a priori* measure of the effectiveness of a minimax search in a given region. There is no such *a priori* measure available for any of the other three points discussed in this section, nor for any of the multivariable search techniques to be considered.

The minimax point has a major drawback—it is quite difficult to calculate for regions of even mildly complicated shape. At present then, the minimax point is more of theoretical than practical interest.

4.05. Median

The first of our measures of effectiveness involved distances only to the extreme points of the region while the second did not use the concept of distance at all. We propose now a criterion which involves the distances to every point of the region, as measured parallel to each of the axes. Let

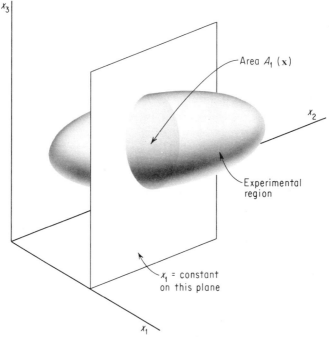

x_1 = constant
on this plane

Fig. 4-5. The element of integration as an area.

$A_i(\mathbf{x})$ be the cross-sectional hyperarea of the intersection of the experimental region with the hyperplane on which x_i is constant (see Fig. 4-5). Then the mean distance $\hat{d}_i(\mathbf{x}')$ in the x_i direction, measured from the point $\mathbf{x}'$ is defined to be

$$\hat{d}_i(\mathbf{x}') \equiv \frac{\int_a^b |x_i - x_i'| A_i(\mathbf{x}) dx_i}{\int_a^b A_i(\mathbf{x}) dx_i} \tag{4-5}$$

The denominator of this expression is, of course, the hypervolume of the experimental region.

We wish to locate $\mathbf{x}'$ so as to minimize each mean distance. To do this we set its derivative with respect to x_i' equal to zero.

$$\frac{d}{dx_i'}\left[\int_a^{x_i'}(x_i' - x_i)A_i(x_i)dx_i - \int_{x_i'}^b(x_i' - x_i)A_i(x_i)dx_i\right]$$

$$= x_i'\frac{d}{dx_i'}\left[\int_a^{x_i'}A_i(x_i)dx_i\right] + \int_a^{x_i'}A_i(x_i)dx_i - x_i'A_i(x_i')$$

$$- x_i'\frac{d}{dx_i'}\left[\int_{x_i'}^b A_i(x_i)dx_i\right] - \int_{x_i'}^b A_i(x_i)dx_i + x_i'A_i(x_i')$$

$$= \int_a^{x'_i} A_i(x_i)\,dx_i - \int_{x'_i}^b A_i(x_i)\,dx_i = 0$$

Thus the components $\hat{x}_i$ of the point $\hat{x}$ for which the mean distances are all minimum must satisfy

$$\int_a^{\hat{x}_i} A_i(x_i)\,dx_i = \int_{\hat{x}_i}^b A_i(x_i)\,dx_i \tag{4-6}$$

Since these two expressions are the hypervolumes of the subregions bounded by the hyperplane for which $x_i = \hat{x}_i$, we shall call the point $\hat{x}$ the *median* or *center of volume*.

Although the median usually will be easier to calculate than the minimax point, the computations will be tedious, often requiring trial and error because each $\hat{x}_i$ appears as a limit of a definite integral. If a high speed computer is available, the computations can be programmed easily, being quite straightforward. In spite of the computation problems, the median is not entirely devoid of interest. For most configurations occurring in practice the contour tangent passing through the median will divide the region into two nearly equal subregions. Thus it often should be pretty close to the minimax point itself, which has the advantages we have already discussed. Although the median is not invariant to rotation of the axes, it does remain insensitive to scale changes.

4.06. Centroid

If we are willing to use the *root mean square distance*, $r_i(\mathbf{x})$, as our criterion of effectiveness, we obtain a point that is much easier to calculate than either the minimax point or the median.
Let

$$r_i(\mathbf{x'}) \equiv \left[\frac{\displaystyle\int_a^b (x_i - x'_i)^2 A_i(x_i)\,dx_i}{\displaystyle\int_a^b A_i(x_i)\,dx_i} \right]^{\frac{1}{2}} \tag{4-7}$$

By setting the derivative of the expression with respect to x'_i equal to zero, we find that $\bar{x}_i$, the value of x'_i where $r_i(x'_i)$ is minimum, is given by

$$\bar{x}_i = \frac{\displaystyle\int_a^b x_i A_i(x_i)\,dx_i}{\displaystyle\int_a^b A_i(x_i)\,dx_i} \tag{4-8}$$

Hence $\bar{x}_i$ is the *centroid* or mean of the region and $r_i(\bar{\mathbf{x}})$ is its *radius of gyration.* Since the *moment of inertia* I_i about the hyperplane $x_i = \bar{x}_i$ is given by

$$I \equiv V r_i^2(\bar{\mathbf{x}})$$

where V is the hypervolume of the region

$$V = \int_a^b A_i(x_i)\, dx_i$$

we see that $\bar{\mathbf{x}}$ is the point about which the moment of inertia and radius of gyration relative to any coordinate $\bar{x}_i$ is minimum.

It is well-known that the centroid is invariant, not only to scale changes, but to rotations as well. Thus the root mean square distance and the moment of inertia about the centroid are minimum in every direction. The calculations needed to find the centroid, involving as they do only evaluations of definite integrals, are much easier than for either the minimax point or the median.

4.07. Pilot experiments

Suppose now that a point **b** in the middle of the region has been selected from among the four suggested, and let **a** represent the point where the old block of experiments was located. The next thing to do is conduct a single *pilot experiment,* not an entire block, at **b**. If the value of the criterion y is greater than at **a**, one feels safe in locating the next block in the vicinity of **b**, determining a new contour tangent, and continuing the exploration.

But what should be done if y turns out to be *less* at **b** than at **a**? In

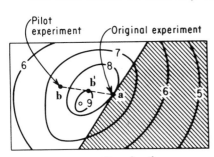

Fig. 4-6. Overshooting.

Fig. 4-6 for example, the criterion drops from 8.0 to 7.2 between block **a** and the pilot experiment at **b**. One could of course put the next block at **b** anyway, confident that the new contour tangent there will be effective in cutting down the region of uncertainty according to whatever criterion of effectiveness was used to locate **b**. There are, however, practical objections to this procedure.

In the first place, optimization explorations are rarely conducted for their own sakes—there is usually a manager involved who has requested the study, and, although knowing little about search technique, is vitally interested in the results of each experiment. A good way to lose such a man's confidence is to carry out a set of experiments which, giving a lower value of y than at the original location, would from his viewpoint be considered "failures." Secondly, such studies often are made on plants actually in production where decreases in y represent actual financial loss. Although a company could tolerate a loss during one or two isolated experiments for the sake of research, it would be expecting too much to ask it to sustain continued losses during an entire block of experiments. Moreover, it is intellectually unsatisfying to concentrate searching effort in regions of low response.

Fortunately, if the response surface is continuous the next block always can be located where y is better than at **a**. Furthermore, the new contour tangent can be made to pass through the pilot point **b** to preserve whatever advantages **b** might have had for cutting down the region of uncertainty. One finds this new location simply by searching for the highest point on the line *between* **a** and **b** (the point **b′** in Fig. 4-6.)

Here is why this procedure works. Since **b** is in the promising region, the criterion y must improve at first as we move away from **a** on the straight line toward **b**. Thus, if the result at **b** is not as good as at **a**, the value of y must go through an optimum somewhere between **a** and **b**, as shown in Fig. 4-7. The step from **a** to **b** is therefore too large, passing completely over a desirable region, as in Figs. 4-6 and 4-7. An obvious remedy is to shorten the step.

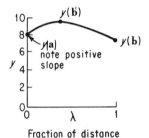

Fig. 4-7. Profile along line from **a** to **b**.

For a more rigorous demonstration that there must be at least one maximum between **a** and **b** one could use Weierstrasse's theorem[†], which asserts that a continuous function in a closed interval always has a maximum inside or on the boundary of the interval. This maximum is clearly not at **b** since $y(\mathbf{b}) < y(\mathbf{a})$. It is not at **a** either, because the slope $dy/d\lambda$ is positive at **a**. Hence the maximum can only be in the interior of the interval. Not that only continuity, not unimodality, is assumed.

Having proven that there must be points between **a** and **b** which give responses better, not only than at **b**, but even that at **a**, we are justified in trying another pilot experiment inside the interval before determining a new contour tangent. If the new result is still not as good as at **a**, we can move even closer to **a** until eventually a point better than **a** is found.

When **b** and **a** are not too widely separated, there is some advantage in trying to locate a relative maximum along the line between them, as

† R. Courant and D. Hilbert, *Methods of Mathematical Physics*, Vol. I (New York: Interscience Publishers, Inc., 1953), p. 164.

at **b**′ in Fig. 4-6. At such a point, the derivative $dy/d\lambda$ vanishes (see Fig. 4-7) which implies that the line is tangent to a contour there. By locating a block of experiments at **b**′, we guarantee that the next contour tangent hyperplane will pass through **b**. This is advantageous because **b** was placed so that any hyperplane through it would cut away a large portion of the remaining experimental region. By following this procedure we may be sure of locating the next block favorably from the standpoint not only of having the criterion higher than at **a**, but also of giving a contour tangent which will significantly reduce the region of uncertainty.

In summary, if the response at **b** is higher that at **a**, locate the next block at **b** without further ado. If not, search out a local maximum on the line so that the next block will give good values of this response and still be effective in reducing the region of uncertainty.

This procedure is illustrated in Fig. 4-8 in which the center of the area of uncertainty remaining after block 3 is indicated by the square marked 3′. The first pilot experiment, marked by a circle 4, gives a yield of 92 percent, the same as at 3. Since this suggests immediately that there must be a high point in the portion between 3 and this experiment, the fourth block is located at point 4. There are in this case only two independent variables, and the new contour tangent is a line, identical with

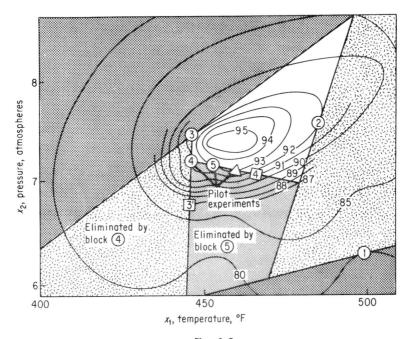

Fig. 4-8.

that between 3 and 3'. The center of the new region of uncertainty is marked by a square containing a 4. An experiment at this point gives a yield of only 91 per cent, lower than at circle 4; so a pilot experiment at circle 5 is in order. The outcome is 93 per cent, a clear improvement, so there must be better points between circle 5 and square 4. A second pilot experiment at the triangle also gives a yield of 93 percent, indicating that the high point is between the two pilot experiments. No more pilot experiments are made in this example; it is assumed that further resolution is not possible. Thus the next block of experiments can be run either at circle 5 or at the triangle. Notice that the first pilot experiment was placed according to the Fibonacci series, one third of the distance from circle 4.

4.08. Summary

The contour tangent search method is an elimination technique of the Kiefer type which can be modified so that it will climb, or at least not descend. Fundamental to the practical success of the method is that the response surface be strongly unimodal and that the experimental error be small. The technique is not affected by the scales of measurement selected, and the need for extrapolation is avoided by exploiting the global property of strong unimodality.

GRADIENT AND ASCENT

Consider a somewhat special optimization problem, an explorer's search for the top of a thickly wooded hill emerging from a flat plain. Even if the density of the forest prevented the explorer from seeing the summit, or even the general shape of the hill, he could eventually reach the top (if it is unimodal) simply by continuing to gain elevation as he walks. Although *any* rising path would take him to the peak, if he is in a hurry he would probably move in directions where the slope of the hill is greatest, provided of course that he does not run into vertical cliffs which he is unwilling to scale.

This intuitively attractive idea of climbing the steepest path forms the basis for a search technique known as the *gradient method,* or the *method of steepest ascent*[†‡]. In the geographical example described above, this direction varies from point to point but is uniquely defined at any particular point. It is in fact the direction perpendicular to the local contour, as

† A. Cauchy, "Méthode générale pour la résolution des systèmes d'équations simultanées," *Compt. rend. Acad. Sci. Paris,* **25** (1847), pp. 536–8.

‡ G. E. P. Box and K. B. Wilson, "On The Experimental Attainment of Optimum Conditions," *J. Roy. Stat. Soc.,* **B13**, 1 (1951).

shown in Fig. 4-9. The method of steepest ascent would locate the next block of experiments somewhere in the direction of the gradient.

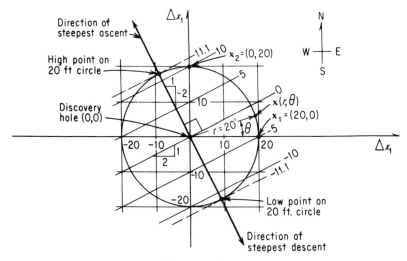

Fig. 4-9. Direction of steepest ascent.

Unlike the contour tangent techniques, the gradient method can be used on *any* unimodal function, not just those that are strongly unimodal. Steepest ascent techniques will work in the presence of experimental error, another advantage. But in many problems the gradient methods require subjective decisions concerning the scales for measuring the independent variables. This defect is rather subtle, stemming from the fact that graphical approaches to physical problems sometimes can lead us unwittingly into non-Euclidean geometry. We shall see that our attempts to apply even such simple Euclidean ideas as "length" and "direction" to physical systems which are non-Euclidean often end in paradox.

Gradient methods being easily misunderstood, we shall be rather detailed when we develop the underlying theory. To begin, we discuss an underground exploration problem which lends itself without difficulty to the method of steepest ascent. Then we describe an industrial problem in which over-active geometric intuition could be deceiving. In studying this second example, which deals with finding the most economical combination of feed temperature and flow rate in a chemical reactor, we encounter the paradox that any of a number of directions can qualify as the direction of *steepest* ascent. For this reason we shall eventually suppress the word "steepest" and speak only of *ascent methods*.

4.09. The gradient

Consider now a hypothetical underground exploration problem. Suppose that geologists have discovered a deposit of mineral ore underneath a flat plain. To bring the ore to the surface it is necessary to sink a vertical mine shaft down to the deposit. If the mining company had complete knowledge about the extent and shape of the deposit, they would of course locate the shaft where the mine tunnels would not have to be too long. Assume, however, that the company does not have this information and that if they want to find out any more about the deposit they must pay for drilling exploratory holes.

Its capital being quite limited, the company needs to start mining ore with as little preliminary expense as possible. The profits from the first production will be used to deepen the shaft to dig further into the deposit. Thus the immediate problem is to find the point where the deposit is nearest the surface, using as few test holes as possible. The geologists set up a rectangular coordinate system on the surface of the plain with its origin at the original discovery hole. The independent variables for the search problem are x_1, the distance east of the origin, and x_2, the distance north of the origin. Holes drilled south or west of the origin are of course given negative coordinates as appropriate. When a new test hole is drilled, the depth at which the ore first appears is recorded. This depth is subtracted from d_0, the depth of the discovery hole, the difference being a convenient criterion of effectiveness y which gets larger as the deposit gets closer to the surface.

$$y \equiv d_0 - d$$

The object of the drilling program is to find the crest of the subterranean hill of minerals, or in more precise terms, the coordinates x_1 and x_2 where the criterion y is maximum.

If the geologist is willing to gamble that the deposit is unimodal in the area of interest, he might wish to use the method of steepest ascent to guide his exploration. This would involve drilling two test holes near the original one to determine the plane tangent to the underground hill in the vicinity of the discovery hole. As described in the earlier discussion on local exploration, one obtains in this way the linear equation of the tangent plane, Eq. (3-18),

$$\varDelta y = m_1 \, \varDelta x_1 + m_2 \, \varDelta x_2$$

which in this case simplifies to

$$y = m_1 x_1 + m_2 x_2 \tag{4-9}$$

because we have defined y to be zero at the origin.

To be specific let us suppose that the first exploratory hole is 20 feet east of the original one and that the deposit is found to be five feet deeper there. Then $x_1 = (20, 0)$ and $y_1 = -5$. Also suppose that the second hole is 20 feet north of the origin and that the deposit there is ten feet closer to the surface: $x_2 = (0, 20)$ and $y_2 = 10$. Then

$$m_1 = \frac{5}{20} = -0.25$$

$$m_2 = \frac{10}{20} = 0.50$$

so that the equation of the tangent plane in the neighborhood of the discovery hole at x_0 is

$$y = -0.25x_1 + 0.50x_2 \tag{4-10}$$

Figure 4-9 is a map showing the locations of the three holes and the contours of the tangent plane at x_0.

The company now wants to explore in the direction where the criterion seems to be increasing the most rapidly, for this is the philosophy of the method of steepest ascent. Let θ be the angle measured from the x_1 axis counterclockwise to any ray emanating from the origin. A point may be identified by its distance r from the origin and the angle θ made by the ray passing through it; this is merely the representation of the point in polar coordinates. The direction of greatest increase in y per unit distance along the ray is the *direction of steepest ascent*. This direction will pass through the highest point on any circle centered on the origin, as in Fig. 4-9, where a radius of 20 feet has been selected to make the circle include the two test holes. The map shows that the two points where the circle is tangent to the straight parallel contours of the tangent plane are the highest and lowest points on the circle. These points locate the directions of steepest *ascent* and *descent* respectively.

The directions of steepest ascent and descent will be found by locating the points on the 20 foot circle where y is greatest and least. In doing so we shall find that these directions are both perpendicular to the contour tangent and hence directly opposite to each other. The coordinates of the points on the circle can be represented entirely as functions of the angle θ:

$$x_1 = 20 \cos \theta \tag{4-11a}$$

$$x_2 = 20 \sin \theta \tag{4-11b}$$

By substituting this parametric representation into Eq. (4-9) we can express the values of the criterion y on the circle as a function only of the angle

$$y = m_1(20 \cos \theta) + m_2(20 \sin \theta)$$

The angle at which y is maximum is that for which the derivative $dy/d\theta$ vanishes.

$$dy/d\theta = -m_1(20 \sin \theta) + m_2(20 \cos \theta) = 0$$

Rather than solve for this angle, we shall use Eq. (4-11) to obtain the rectangular coordinoates x_1^* and x_2^* of the high point.

$$\frac{x_2^*}{x_1^*} = \frac{m_2}{m_1} \qquad (4\text{-}12)$$

Notice that this equation is valid for circles of any radius since the radius cancels out. This derivation follows that of Phillips[†].

In this numerical example, the ratio m_2/m_1 is equal to -2. Therefore the high point is where the line

$$x_2 = -2x_1 \qquad (4\text{-}12)$$

intersects the circle

$$\sqrt{x_1^2 + x_2^2} = 20$$

There are, however, two points of intersection, one at $(-4\sqrt{5}, 8\sqrt{5})$ and the other at $(4\sqrt{5}, -8\sqrt{5})$, because the derivative $dy/d\theta$ also vanishes where y is minimum on the circle. But Eq. (4-10) shows that it is the former point that gives the maximum because its coordinates have respectively the same signs as the coefficients m_1 and m_2, making each term in the equation positive.

$$y(-4\sqrt{5}, 8\sqrt{5}) = (-0.25)(-4\sqrt{5}) + 0.50(8\sqrt{5}) = 5\sqrt{5}$$

On the other hand, the coordinates of the other point, having signs opposite from those of the maximum point, make every term negative, indicating that the former point is at the minimum. The direction of steepest ascent is therefore exactly opposite to the direction of steepest descent.

It is instructive to compare the Eq. (4-12) for the gradient line with that for the contour tangent obtained by setting $y = 0$ in Eq. (4-9).

$$\frac{x_2}{x_1} = -\frac{m_2}{m_1}$$

Since the slopes of the two lines are negative reciprocals of each other, they are perpendicular, an elementary fact of analytic geometry. Thus when there are only two independent variables the direction of steepest ascent can be found graphically by drawing a line perpendicular to the contour.

† H. B. Phillips, *Vector Analysis* (New York, John Wiley & Sons, Inc., 1949).

The mining company should not, of course, drill their next hole at $(4\sqrt{5}, -8\sqrt{5})$ for this would be too close to the discovery hole to justify the expense. They prefer to go far away in the hope of finding where the deposit is much closer to the surface. The line of steepest ascent may be represented parametrically in terms of the distance r from the origin by writing

$$r = \sqrt{x_1^2 + x_2^2} = \frac{x_1}{m_1}\sqrt{m_1^2 + m_2^2}$$

whence

$$x_1 = \frac{m_1 r}{\sqrt{m_1^2 + m_2^2}} = \frac{-\sqrt{5}\, r}{5} = -0.447r \qquad (4\text{-}13a)$$

Similarly,

$$x_2 = \frac{m_2 r}{\sqrt{m_1^2 + m_2^2}} = 0.894r \qquad (4\text{-}13b)$$

The extrapolated estimate of the criterion is therefore

$$y = r\sqrt{m_1^2 + m_2^2} = 0.557r \qquad (4\text{-}14)$$

Notice that to make y positive we must make r greater than zero; negative values lead us in the direction of steepest *descent*. The absolute value of r is the distance from the origin, and the slope in the direction of steepest ascent is 0.557 feet of rise per foot of distance.

Although the mining company now knows the most desirable direction in which to pursue their search, they have no idea how far from the original hole it is safe to go, and the method of steepest ascent cannot help them decide. They must weigh the possibly greater improvements at large distances against the danger that the gradient will change direction sharply, because the method of steepest ascent, being based entirely on a determination of a local gradient, inherently involves extrapolation. But if the next test hole is unsuccessful, the exploration team can always move back toward the origin until they find an improvement, for reasons we discussed in the preceding section on pilot experiments. As soon as one of these pilot holes along the gradient line shows improvement, the new direction of steepest ascent can be redetermined at the more promising site. This procedure may be repeated as long as the potential gains appear to outweigh drilling expenses.

4.10. Multidimensional generalization

The notion of gradient, or direction of steepest ascent, may be generalized to functions of k independent variables. If the linear approximation has the form

$$\Delta y = \sum_{i=1}^{k} m_i \, \Delta x_i \tag{4-15}$$

then the gradient line is represented parametrically by

$$\Delta x_i = m_i \lambda \qquad i = 1, 2, \dots, k \tag{4-16}$$

where λ is the arbitrary parameter of the line. Equations 4-15 and 4-16 together give.

$$\Delta y = \lambda \sum_{i=1}^{k} m_i^2$$

Hence Δy increases with λ, and positive values of λ generate the line of steepest *ascent*. Conversely, the line of steepest *descent* is the set of points for which λ is negative.

As an illustration consider the function

$$y = -2x_1^2 - x_2^2 - 3x_3^2 - 2x_4^2 \tag{4-17}$$

Suppose we wish to search along the line of steepest ascent from the point $p = (-1, 0, 3, -2)$. The linear approximation to y at this point is obtained by direct differentiation in this artificial example, since the function y has been given in advance. This approximation, which corresponds to Eq. (4-15), is

$$\Delta y = 4 \, \Delta x_1 + 0 \, \Delta x_2 - 18 \, \Delta x_3 + 8 \, \Delta x_4$$

with $\Delta x_1 \equiv x_1 + 1$, $\Delta x_2 \equiv x_2$, $\Delta x_3 \equiv x_3 - 3$, and $\Delta x_4 \equiv x_4 + 2$ in the usual manner. Eq. (4-16) gives the parametric equations of the line of steepest ascent as

$$\Delta x_1 = 4\lambda, \qquad \Delta x_2 = 0, \qquad \Delta x_3 = -18\lambda; \qquad \Delta x_4 = 8\lambda$$

or

$$x_1 = -1 + 4\lambda, \qquad x_2 = 0, \qquad x_3 = 3 - 18\lambda, \qquad x_4 = -2 + 8\lambda \tag{4-18}$$

The four equations in the five variables have one degree of freedom, as we would expect for a line. A typical point on the line of steepest ascent is specified by selecting any positive λ, say $\lambda = 2$. The corresponding point is $(7, 0, -33, 14)$. The reader may verify that the point $(1, 0, -6, 2)$ is on the line of steepest *descent* (what would the corresponding λ be ?).

Since all the points on the line have been expressed in terms of a single parameter, the values that the function y takes along the line can also be made a function of λ alone. Equations (4-17) and (4-18) together give.

$$y = -2(-1 + 4\lambda)^2 - 3(3 - 18\lambda)^2 - 2(-2 + 8\lambda)^2$$

The value of λ giving maximum y on the line can now be obtained by differentiating the above equation with respect to λ:

$$\frac{dy}{d\lambda} = 404 - 2264\lambda = 0$$

whence $\lambda = 0.179$ gives the highest value of y on the line of steepest ascent. The corresponding point is $(-0.22, 0, -0.22, -0.58)$.

The line of steepest ascent will always be characterized parametrically by one equation for each of the k coordinates. There being $k + 1$ variables in all (counting λ), the set of points represented always has one degree of freedom. Since the equations are linear, the points must lie on a straight line in space. Parameterization enables us to work with one dimension instead of k coordinates, simplifying things both algebraically and conceptually. In practice, when the function is not known in advance, the high point on a gradient line can be found by the powerful unidimensional techniques developed in Chap. 2. Thus λ may be used as the independent variable for a Fibonacci search. Most of the multivariable search methods we shall study will involve breaking the problem down into a sequence of unidimensional searches.

4.11. A non-Euclidean paradox

In our mine exploration example we had no trouble defining length and direction unambiguously because the problem was describable in terms of the ordinary Euclidean geometry developed long ago to assist land surveyors. We shall study next a common industrial problem in which length and direction lose their ordinary meaning. As this non-Euclidean world will seem paradoxical to anyone who tries to apply Euclid's deductions to it indiscriminately, we shall enter it slowly and cautiously. It will soon become apparent that we must be very careful about choosing scales of measurement of the independent variables. Indeed, we shall find that we can, by appropriate adjustment of the scales, make any of a great many directions into the "gradient direction."

Consider then a hypothetical chemical manufacturer whose problem is to obtain the most profitable operating conditions for one of his processes. In this process a raw material is heated so that it will undergo a chemical transformation which converts it into a marketable product tainted by impurities formed during the reaction. These undesirable side products are then removed by a separation process whose cost cannot be ignored. In practice many factors can affect the economics of such a process, but we shall for simplicity consider only two—time and temperature.

The time spent in the reactor by the material is important because it limits the production rate of the process. Any reduction in this processing time will, other things being equal, increase the production rate. Temperature affects the rate of all chemical reactions taking place. Moderate increases in temperature speed up the reaction producing the main product and thus make possible higher production rates. Unfortunately, high temperatures also quicken the undesirable reactions that form impurities or that burn up the main product. Obviously a large holding time should not be combined with a high temperature, for this would merely produce small quantities of low-quality product. Similarly, it would be infeasible to feed the raw material too rapidly to a low-temperature reactor, for this would leave large quantities unconverted that would have to be recovered from the product and run again. Thus the profit contours on a graph of temperature (x_2) versus holding time (x_1) would look something like Fig. 4.9.

Suppose the manufacturer has just put a new process into operation. According to the estimates of his process designers the best operating conditions should be in the neighborhood of five minutes holding time and 1000°C temperature, so the first run is made under these conditions. The corresponding profit rate is measured as $10 per minute. To see how this profit behaves in the vicinity of the base case, the chief engineer calls for two test runs, one 20°C higher in temperature and the other 20 seconds longer in time. We shall assume, in order to make the numbers of this problem similar to those of the mine exploration example, that the changes in profit for these trials are respectively −5 cents and +10 cents. Taking Δx_1 to be the change in temperature, Δx_2 to be the change in holding time, and Δy to be the corresponding change in profit rate, we find that the coefficients that held for Eq. (3-55) are also valid here.

$$\Delta y = -0.25\,\Delta x_1 + 0.50\,\Delta x_2 \qquad (4\text{-}19)$$

Let us try to apply the method of steepest ascent to this problem. It would at first glance seem reasonable to plot contours of the criterion y as functions of the temperature x_1 and holding time x_2 as we did in the mine exploration example. Using ordinary rectangular coordinate graph paper we could obtain a "map" identical with that of Fig. 4-9 if we represented one degree centigrade and one minute by the same number of scale divisions on the graph. This procedure of selecting scales, which most of us carry out more or less subconsciously, can be formalized by letting s_1 and s_2 be the scales of measurement of x_1 and x_2—the quantities of x_1 and x_2 associated with a unit length along the axes of the graph paper. Thus s_1 is the number of degrees Centigrade per graph division and s_2 is the number of minutes holding time per graph division. Our first choice of scales was such that $s_1 = s_2$, and in this case the gradient line is described by Eq. (4-12)

$$\Delta x_2 = -2\,\Delta x_1 \qquad (4\text{-}12)$$

In the mine exploration example the vertical and horizontal scales were equal. It would have been absurd to make them different, for in plane geometry 20 feet north involves the same distance as 20 feet measured in a westerly, or any other, direction. One cannot, however, make the same sort of comparison between a degree centigrade and a minute of time. For this reason, it is not at all necessary to have the vertical temperature scale equal to the horizontal time scale in our chemical processing problem. In practice one simply selects scales that fit the problem comfortably onto whatever graph paper happens to be at hand.

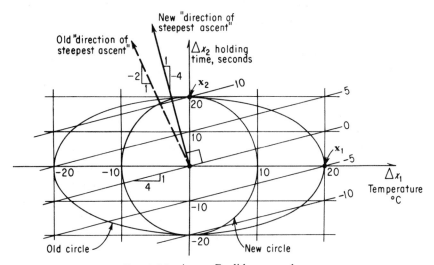

Fig. 4-10. A non-Euclidean paradox.

Just to see what happens, let us cut the temp. scale s_1 in half, so that $s_2 = 2s_1$. As shown in Fig. 4-10, this change of scale stretches the horizontal temp. axis to twice its original length, and the slopes of all lines appear to be half of those in Fig. 4-9. Thus, although Eq. (4-19), which describes the contour tangent, is unaffected by this arbitrary scale change,

$$\Delta x_2 = 0.50 \, \Delta x_1$$

the slope of the contour tangent will only be 0.25 for the new temp. scale. Similarly, the slope of the line described by Eq. (4-12) becomes -1, clearly not the negative reciprocal of the contour tangent slope (0.25). Therefore, the line which was the gradient in Fig. 4-9 is not the direction of steepest ascent in Fig. 4-10. This new gradient, perpendicular to the to the contour tangent, must have a slope of -4, which means that its equation is

$$\Delta x_2 = -8 \, \Delta x_1$$

The new gradient is also shown in Fig. 4-10.

To verify that this new gradient line is really the apparent direction of steepest ascent, we have drawn a circle about the origin. It is clear that the highest point on this circle lies on the new gradient line. Because of the scale change, this circle does not pass through both experimental points as did the circle in Fig. 4-9. In fact, the points on the circle of Fig. 4-9 are distorted into an ellipse in Fig. 4-10. The highest point on this ellipse lies of course on the old gradient line.

We now have two different Eqs., (4-12) and (4-20), each one representing the points on a "gradient line." In fact, any equation of the form

$$\Delta x_i = c_i \frac{m_i}{|m_i|} \lambda, \qquad i = 1, 2, \ldots, k$$

Where the c_i are *arbitrary* positive constants, can be the parametric equation of a line of steepest ascent. Thus, in the problem we have been studying, any straight line in the proper quadrant can, by appropriate adjustment of the scales be made into a gradient line. Let us get to the bottom of this paradox.

4.12. Distance, scale, and dimensional inhomogeneity

The preceding geometric demonstrations have been intended to make plausible the assertion that in many physical problems there is no unique direction of steepest ascent. There are only directions which go up, those which go down, and those which are horizontal. To measure "steepness" one must be able to define distance satisfactorily in all directions, not just those parallel to the x_1-x_2 axes. This is easy in geometric situations where length is well defined in every direction, as in the mine exploration example. In such cases, distance r between two points is given by the theorem of Pythagoras

$$r = \sqrt{(\Delta x_1)^2 + (\Delta x_2)^2} \qquad (4\text{-}21)$$

This unambiguous definition of distance permits us to draw the circle of constant distance from the origin that was needed to locate the direction of steepest ascent. A space in which distance can be defined by Eq. (4-21) is said to be *Euclidean*.

Distance cannot be defined this way in the chemical reactor study. Even if we applied Eq. (4-21) in a purely formal manner we would be trying to add "square degrees Centigrade" [the units of $(\Delta x_1)^2$] to "square minutes" [the units of $(\Delta x_2)^2$]. One would also encounter dimensional inhomogeneity in Eq. (4-12), which defines the direction of steepest ascent.

$$\frac{x_2^*}{x_1^*} = \frac{m_2}{m_1} \qquad (4\text{-}12)$$

The coefficient m_1 is the partial derivative $(\partial y / \partial x_1)$ and therefore must have the dimensions of profit rate per unit change in temperature. Similarly, m_2 will have the dimensions of profit rate per unit holding time, and the ratio m_2/m_1, will have dimensions of temperature/time. This is inconsistent with the dimensions of the left member of the Eq. (4-12), which must have the dimensions time/temperature.

It is tempting to try circumventing this annoying difficulty by plotting the contours on paper, for graph paper is safely Euclidean even if the original problem is not. In doing this we would not longer be dealing with the physical variables x_1 and x_2 with all their irritating dimensions. We would instead be working with the transformed variables x_1' and x_2' defined by

$$x_1' \equiv \frac{x_1}{s_1}$$

and

$$x_2' \equiv \frac{x_2}{s_2}$$

where s_1 and s_2 are the scales chosen. These new variables all would have the dimensions of length, their units being the scale divisions on the graph. In terms of the transformed variables we may define distance r' to be

$$r' = \sqrt{(\Delta x_1')^2 + (\Delta x_2')^2} \qquad (4\text{-}22)$$

In the space generated by these transformed variables, the criterion y would be expressed as

$$\Delta y = m_1' \, \Delta x_1' + m_2' \, \Delta x_2' \qquad (4\text{-}23)$$

where

$$m_1' = \frac{m_1}{s_1} \qquad (4\text{-}24a)$$

$$m_2' = \frac{m_2}{s_2} \qquad (4\text{-}24b)$$

The equation of the gradient in the Euclidean space of the graph paper is therefore

$$\frac{\Delta x_2'}{\Delta x_1'} = \frac{m_2'}{m_1'} \qquad (4\text{-}25)$$

which can be verified by running through the derivation given previously in the mine exploration example. In terms of the original physical variables, the direction of steepest ascent is given by

$$\frac{\Delta x_2}{\Delta x_1} = \left(\frac{s_1}{s_2}\right)^2 \frac{m_2}{m_1} \tag{4-26}$$

Equation (4-12) for the Euclidean direction of steepest ascent is therefore a special case of Eq. (4-26) in which the two scales are identical. In view of the dependence of the direction of steepest ascent on the scales used, we prefer to omit the word "steepest" and speak only of *ascent methods*.

4.13. Choice of scale

Ascent methods are important because they work on any unimodal function, while contour tangent elimination must be confined to strongly unimodal criteria of effectiveness. No matter what scales are chosen, ascent methods will eventually find the peak, and if the scales are selected wisely, convergence can be rapid.

Buehler, Shah, and Kempthorne[†] have studied the effect of scales on speed of convergence of ascent techniques. Considering quadratic functions having ellipsoidal contours, they found that the best choice of scales would be that making the contours as nearly spherical as possible. This is not surprising, because for spherical contours all gradient lines pass through the maximum.

Their rules, although developed only for the limited class of quadratic functions, seem to us good ones to follow in general, which is why we listed them in Sec. 1.08 on representation and scaling. The rules are (1) select scales of measurement in which a unit change in one independent variable *at the optimum* gives the same change in the dependent variable as a unit change in any other factor, and (2) prefer representations in which the independent variables do not interact; that is, in which there are no terms involving functions of more than one independent variable.

The information needed to follow these rules is not always available, and in its absence one is forced to guess. While we can hope that theoretical knowledge about a particular system being optimized will lead to scaling estimates that aren't too bad, it should be remembered that for a given response surface and starting point, the rate of convergence for the ascent method "may be arbitrarily slow for a sufficiently poor choice of units[‡]."

[†] R. J. Buehler, B. V. Shah and O. Kempthorne, "Some Properties of Steepest Ascent and Related Procedures for Finding Optimum Conditions," Iowa State University Statistical Laboratory (April 1961), pp. 8–10, 18.

[‡] Buehler, Shah, and Kempthorne, *op. cit.*, p. 17.

4.14. Saddles

A great advantage of gradient methods, one that is not widely re-cognized, is that they will inherently stay away from saddlepoints. Herbert Zellnick has told us that the gradient search computer program developed by him and his colleagues[†] at Scientific Design, Inc. avoids saddles so dependably that the only way they could test their subroutine for exploring the neighborhood of a pass was to start the search there. Figure 4-11, in which gradient lines (dashed) are superimposed on the contours of a bimodal response surface, suggests why. Only one gradient line out of the infinite number possible actually passes through the saddle. The other lines all lead directly to one peak or the other. Hence the possibility of a gradient method's stumbling upon a saddle is quite remote, although the prudent experimenter should still check at the end of a search to see if he has, by chance, found a saddle instead of a peak.

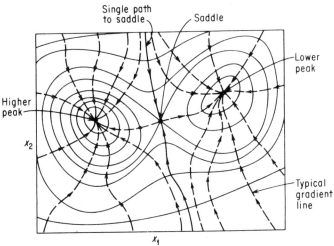

Fig. 4-11. Gradient lines in the presence of a saddle.

4.15. Summary

Ascent methods seek a maximum by climbing rather than by elimina-tion as do contour tangent procedures. Gradient, or "steepest" ascent techniques are in many physical situations linked intimately to a more or less arbitrary selection of units or scales of measurement. Such procedures tend naturally to avoid saddlepoints. They will eventually converge for

‡ H. E. Zellnick, N. E. Sondak, and R. S. Davis, "Gradient Search Optimization," *Chem. Eng. Progr.*, **58**, 8 (1962), pp. 35–41.

any unimodal function, even when there is appreciable experimental error. For strongly unimodal functions, the ascent and elimination techniques can be combined if desired.

EXERCISES

1. For the right triangle whose corners are the points $(0, 0)$, $(1, 0)$, and $(0, 1)$, find the coordinates of the
   (a) midpoint.
   (b) minimax point.
   (c) median.
   (d) centroid.

2. For the right triangle whose corners are the points $(0, 0)$, $(\sqrt{2}/2, \sqrt{2}/2)$, $(\sqrt{2}/2, -\sqrt{2}/2)$, find the coordinates of the
   (a) midpoint.
   (b) minimax point.
   (c) median.
   (d) centroid.

3. Search for the maximum of the function $y = \exp(-x_1^2 - 4x_2^2 - 9x_3^2)$ in the experimental region $-1 \leq x_i \leq 3 (i = 1, 2, 3)$ by applying contour tangent elimination once. State whether you are using midpoints, medians, or centroids. Give the area of the final interval of uncertainty as your result. Also report the values of y attained at each step. To save time, obtain the contour tangents by differentiating y rather than by taking direct measurements.

4. Apply the method of steepest ascent to the preceding problem twice, locating each new block at the high point along the preceding line of steepest ascent. Report values of y attained at each step. Save time by using direct differentiation wherever possible.

5. Plot four contour tangents and four gradient lines for the following functions in the region $-2 \leq x_1 \leq 2$, $-2 \leq x_2 \leq 2$.
   (a) $\exp(-x_1^2 - 4x_2^2)$
   (b) $\ln(x_1^2 + 4x_2^2)$
   (c) $x_1^2 + 4x_2^3$
   (d) $x_1 x_2$
   (e) $x_1^2 + x_2^2$

6. A function y depends on four independent variables x_1, x_2, x_3, and x_4, and the following table gives the measured value of y at eight different points.
   (a) Give the coordinates of any point on the line of steepest *ascent* passing through $(0, 1, -1, 3)$ [Do not give $(0, 1, -1, 3)$ as answer].
   (b) Give the coordinates of any point [except $(0, 1, -1, 3)$] in the contour tangent hyper-plane passing through $(0, 1, -1, 3)$.

DATA

x_1	x_2	x_3	x_4	y
0	1	−1	3	5
1	1	−1	3	7
2	1	−1	3	9
−1	2	−1	3	2
0	−1	−1	3	7
0	1	1	3	7
0	1	−1	2	5
0	2	0	3	5

7. It is desired to find the point where an unknown function y is maximum on the line between the two points $(1, -1, 0, 2)$ and $(-5, -1, 3, 1)$.

   (a) Assuming perfect resolution and unimodality of the function on the line, give the coordinates of the points where you would measure the function next, assuming you are going to conduct a total of five new experiments in sequence.

   (b) What is the final interval of uncertainty on the coordinate x_1 ?

Acceleration
Along a Ridge

5

> *"Beware the pine-tree's withered branch!*
> *Beware the awful avalanche!"*
> *This was the peasant's last Good-night,*
> *A voice replied, far up the height,*
> *Excelsior!*
>
> *—Longfellow*

Having studied the geometry and algebra of tangents and gradients, we are ready for more sophisticated multivariable search procedures. As the chapter title suggests, these techniques involve acceleration of the convergence of the methods already described. This acceleration is accomplished by exploiting the fact that most response surfaces have one or more ridges leading to the optimum. Thus if one can get on a ridge and follow it, one can reach the summit quickly.

The concept of "ridge" will be introduced by examining the behavior of the very simple strategy of adjusting only one independent variable at a time while holding the others fixed. It will be seen that when the variables interact strongly a ridge will be generated that will slow down or even completely confound this technique. This drawback can usually be avoided by using gradient methods, but even they will zig-zag more or less on a ridge depending on the angle at which they strike it. We shall see that "ridge" is in fact a rather loose term whose geographic overtones can be misleading. After defining more precisely the idea of a "resolution ridge," based on how finely distinct values of the dependent variable can be detected, we shall be ready to study the acceleration techniques which are the main topic of this chapter.

Two types of acceleration scheme can be distinguished—those effective on straight ridges and those which will follow curved ones. For straight ridges the method of parallel tangents (*partan*) of Shah, Buehler, and Kempthorne[†] would appear efficient. A variant of this method seems to have been discovered independently by Powell[‡]. When the response hypersurface contours are concentric ellipsoids, partan will locate the optimum *exactly* after no more than $2k - 1$ unidimensional optimizations (k is the number of independent variables), and the technique can be applied to other functions as well, although its performance is predictable only on ellipsoids.

On curved ridges the *direct search* techniques have proven successful. The idea of direct search is to use past successes to guide the placement of future experiments, keeping the computations as simple as possible. The *pattern search* technique of Hooke and Jeeves[§], developed further by Wood[ǁ], has had reasonable practical success, probably due to its ability to follow a curved ridge when necessary. Mugele's[#] "poor man's optimizer" scheme also is able to track curved ridges. The more elaborate technique of Rosenbrock[††], which we shall call the *rotating coordinate* method, has out-performed all contenders on a difficult two-dimensional curved ridge concocted to test it out. A. Harkins[‡‡] has found partan to give performance comparable even to Rosenbrock's method, at least on this particular test function.

5.01. Sectioning

Perhaps the first scheme that might occur to an experimenter would be to alter one independent variable until the criterion ceases to improve, then to change another variable, and so forth. We shall see that this *sectioning* or *one-at-a-time* method, described by Friedman and Savage[§§],

[†] B. V. Shah, R. J. Buehler, and O. Kempthorne, The Method of Parallel Tangents (PARTAN) for Finding an Optimum," Technical Report No. 2, Office of Naval Research Contract Nonr-530(05), Iowa State University Statistical Laboratory, Ames (Apr. 1961, rev. Aug. 1962).

[‡] M. J. D. Powell, "An Iterative Method for Finding Stationary Values of a Function of Several Variables," *Computer J.* 5, 2 (July 1962), pp. 147–51.

[§] R. Hooke and T. A. Jeeves, "Direct Search Solution of Numerical and Statistical Problems," *J. Assoc. Comp. Mach.*, 8, 2 (Apr. 1962), pp. 212–29.

[ǁ] C. F. Wood, "Application of Direct Search to the Solution of Engineering Problems," Westinghouse Scientific paper 6-4-1210-1-P.

[#] R. A. Mugele, "A Nonlinear Digital Optimizing Program for Process Control Systems," *Proc. Western Joint Computer Conf.* (1962).

[††] H. H. Rosenbrock, "An Automatic Method for Finding the Greatest or Least Value of a Function," *Computer J.*, 3, 3 (Oct. 1960), pp. 175–84.

[‡‡] A. Harkins, personal communication (Mar. 1963).

[§§] M. Friedman and L. S. Savage, *Selected Techniques of Statistical Analysis* (New York: McGraw-Hill Book Co., Inc., 1947).

will not always reach the maximum, even when the contours are convex. Hence, even though its performance is scale-invariant, its performance is often so poor that its practical value is extremely limited.

The simple sectioning method described by Friedman and Savage involves altering only one variable at a time, holding all the others constant. One therefore searches for the high point on the straight line described by $\Delta x_i = 0$ for all $i \neq j$, where j is the identifying index of the variable adjusted. Once this high point is found, x_i is fixed and some other variable altered. This procedure is continued until no further improvement is possible. Since each leg of the search will be parallel to one of the coordinate axes, for two independent variables the search path will resemble the staircase shown in Fig. 5-1.

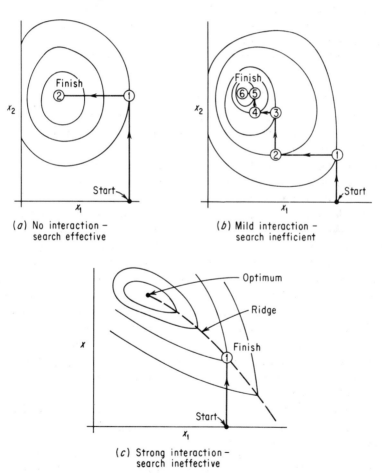

(a) No interaction –
search effective

(b) Mild interaction –
search inefficient

(c) Strong interaction –
search ineffective

Fig. 5-1. Sectional search.

Figure 5-1 demonstrates how dependent is the performance of the one-at-a-time method on the shapes of the contours. It is highly effective for circles or ellipses having their major and minor axes parallel to the coordinate axes. This would mean that the independent variables are not interacting. But when the major and minor axes are tilted, as in Fig. 5-1(b), the method is forced to change direction many times before reaching the optimum. The method fails completely when the response surface has a sharp ridge as in Fig. 5-1(c), for, being unable to move diagonally, it cannot find any higher places once it reaches the ridge where the contours come to a point. This possibility of getting stuck on a ridge led Box and Wilson to devise their ascent method for exploring in directions not parallel to the coordinate axes[†]. Buehler, Shah, and Kempthorne[‡] have shown how the ridge structure affects the performance of sectioning, which is, incidentally, totally independent of scale considerations. They concluded that the method, uncombined with other techniques, is not suitable unless the experimenter knows in advance that such ridges are absent.

5.02. Resolution ridges

Before studying other methods, we must understand what a "ridge" is and how it affects the search for an optimum. The geographic concept "ridge" is not sufficiently precise for our purposes, and we shall have to define the special idea of a *resolutuion ridge* in order to discuss ridge following methods unambiguously. Before introducing this new concept, let us see what is unsuitable about the geographic one.

Consider two men viewing a mountain from two different positions, as in Fig. 5-2. Mr. *A* would say that the points on curve *A* would be on the "ridge," since from where he stands these points form the profile of the mountain. On the other hand, Mr. *B* would see a different "ridge." In fact, any point on the mountain which can be seen at all will, from some viewpoint, be on a "ridge." If there are some points that appear to be on a ridge when seen from many different angles, they will often be called the "crest of the ridge," and if the points are all about the same elevation the whole mountain may be called a "ridge." Thus the geographic idea of "ridge," while helping us picture the formation or response surface with which we are dealing, is not precise enough to be useful in analyzing ridge climbing techniques.

We prefer to define a "ridge" as the locus of points where the one-

[†] G. E. P. Box and K. B. Wilson, "The Experimental Attainment of Optimum Conditions," *J. Roy. Stat. Soc.*, **B13** (1951), p. 1.

[‡] R. J. Buehler, B. N. Shah and O. Kempthorne, "Some Properties of Steepest Ascent and Related Procedures for Finding Optimum Conditions," Iowa State University Statistical Laboratory, Ames, Iowa (April 1961).

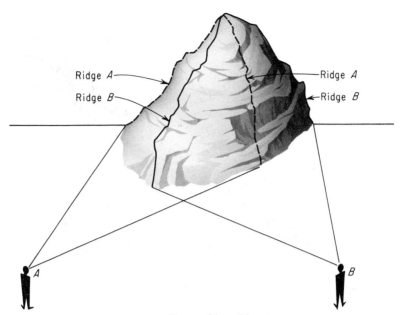

Fig. 5-2. Geographic "ridges."

at-a-time method will stop before reaching the optimum. Hence any point on a *ridge* will be the best attainable in any direction parallel to the co-ordinate axes. Such a ridge is shown in Fig. 5-1(c); the other two response surfaces in Fig. 5-1 do not have ridges according to this definition.

A ridge of this sort can occur only where the contour lies entirely in one quadrant (for two variables; the multidimensional generalization of the quadrant is called an *orthant*). This can only happen if the contour comes to a sharp point, meaning that the first derivatives are discontinuous there. Practically speaking, however, the fact that observations must be a finite distance from each other to be distinguishable can cause a sectional search to hang up even when the contours are smooth. Let $\epsilon_i (> 0)$ be the closest distance between two points on a line parallel to the x_i axis for which a difference between the results can be detected. That is, ϵ_i, the *resolution* in the x_i direction, is such that for all $x_1, \ldots, x_i, \ldots, x_k$ it can be asserted that

$$y(x_1, \ldots, x_i, \ldots, x_k) \neq y(x_1, \ldots, x_i + \epsilon_i, \ldots, x_k)$$

A point $(x_1, \ldots, x_i, \ldots, x_k)$ will be said to be on a *resolution ridge* if it is above all points $(x_1, \ldots, x_i + \epsilon_i, \ldots, x_k)$ and $(x_1, \ldots, x_i - \epsilon_i, \ldots, x_k)$. If a point is *below* all such neighboring points it will be said to be in a *resolution valley*. Resolution ridges are important in maximization problems. A resolution ridge may be a region rather than a line. As shown

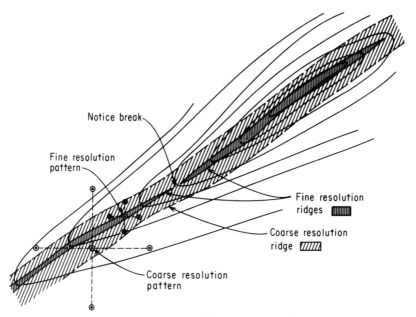

Notice break

Fine resolution
pattern

Fine resolution
ridges

Coarse resolution
ridge

Coarse resolution
pattern

Fig. 5-3. Coarse and fine resolution ridges.

in Fig. 5-3, a resolution ridge becomes narrower as the resolution is made finer. With sufficient resolution, a ridge may even vanish.

The one-at-a-time method will not reach the peak if it runs into a resolution ridge. On the other hand, the contour tangent elimination method is not particularly confounded by a ridge; it will merely lead to a long narrow region of uncertainty. Ascent methods can safely navigate a ridge, but unless one fortunately steers right up the ridge there is liable to be a lot of inefficient zig-zagging, as shown in Fig. 5-5. The parallel tangents and pattern search techniques about to be described will find the trend of a resolution ridge and move rapidly along it.

PARALLEL TANGENTS

The first acceleration technique to be described is the method of parallel tangents, invented by Shah, Buehler, and Kempthorne.[†] *Partan,* as they call the technique, combines many desirable properties of the simpler

[†] B. V. Shah, R. J. Buehler, and O. Kempthorne, "The Method of Parallel Tangents (PARTAN) for Finding an Optimum," Technical Report No. 2, Office of Naval Research Contract Nonr-530(05), Iowa State University Statistical Laboratory, Ames, Iowa (April 1961, rev. Aug. 1962). See also "Some Algorithms for Minimizing a Function of Several Variables," to appear in *Soc. Ind. Appl. Math. Journ.*

methods already described. It can climb like the ascent methods. Its behavior can be made invariant to changes in scales of measurement. Since the basic geometric properties measured are contour tangents, it can be used as an elimination technique. Its master strategy is based on certain global properties of ellipsoids. For criterion functions with concentric ellipsoidal contours, partan will find the optimum exactly after a fixed, small number of measurements. But even when the contours are not precisely elliptical, the technique has certain ridge following properties which make it attractive when the ridges are straight. Consequently partan may be considered a master strategy integrating and guiding the opening, middle, and end game tactics already described.

We have two aims in studying partan. First, the power and elegance of partan demand its inclusion in any book dealing with experimental search methods. But almost as important, the study of partan permits us to translate some useful geometric concepts into exercises with which the reader can test his understanding of multidimensional geometry.

5.03. Accelerated Ascent

Suppose, for some fortunate choice of representation and scale, that a unimodal response surface representing a function of two variables is a surface of revolution. The contours for such a function would be concentric circles with the maximum at the center, as shown in Fig. 5-4. One could locate its peak by measuring the contour tangent at any point **a** and then locating the high point on the gradient line through **a**. In general if a function of an arbitrary number of variables has contours which are concentric hyperspheres, the search will still only take a single unidimensional exploration along the gradient line from any point, for in such circumstances all gradient lines are straight and pass through the peak.

Usually we will not be so lucky in our selection of scale and representation, and we must consider the possibility of concentric ellipsoidal

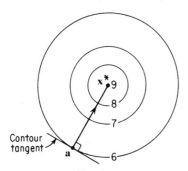

Fig. 5-4. Circular contours.

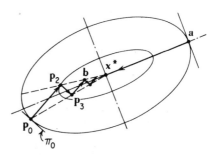

Fig. 5-5. Elliptical contours.

contours as in Fig. 5-5. Let us again apply the method of steepest ascent for this particular choice of scale. If, as at point **a**, our first point happens to be precisely on one of the axes of the system of ellipses, the gradient line will pass right through the peak and the search will be over in one ascent. Otherwise the search will follow a zig-zag course such as the one from $\mathbf{p}_0$ to $\mathbf{p}_2$ to $\mathbf{p}_3$ to **b**, and so on. It is interesting to notice that in principle the steep ascent search will not reach the peak in a finite number of steps because the steps shorten as the maximum is approached. However, the peak can be approached as closely as desired, and if the starting point is not too near the major axis the neighborhood of the peak is attained rapidly.

Notice that the crooked path is bounded by two straight lines which intersect at the peak. This suggests that the search from point $\mathbf{p}_3$ be conducted, not in the gradient direction toward **b**, but along the straight line from $\mathbf{p}_0$ through $\mathbf{p}_3$. In this way the peak would be located exactly after three unidimensional searches: first from $\mathbf{p}_0$ to $\mathbf{p}_2$ along the gradient at $\mathbf{p}_0$, then from $\mathbf{p}_2$ to $\mathbf{p}_3$ along the gradient at $\mathbf{p}_2$, and finally from $\mathbf{p}_3$ along the line through $\mathbf{p}_0$ and $\mathbf{p}_3$. This sort of acceleration of steepest ascent search was first proposed by Forsythe and Motzkin.[†] It is the two-dimensional version of what will be called *steep ascent partan*. In this exposition we have identified the starting point as $\mathbf{p}_0$ rather than $\mathbf{p}_1$ for reasons that will become clear later when we generalize the technique to many dimensions.

5.04. Plane general partan

Notice in Fig. 5-5 that the line $\mathbf{p}_3$-$\mathbf{p}_2$ is parallel to the tangent line π_0

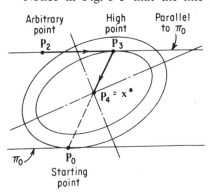

Arbitrary point P_2 High point P_3 Parallel to π_0

$P_4 = \mathbf{x}^*$

π_0 P_0
Starting point

Fig. 5-6. General partan in two dimensions.

at the point $\mathbf{p}_0$. The point $\mathbf{p}_3$ is the high point on $\mathbf{p}_3$-$\mathbf{p}_2$, and $\mathbf{p}_0$ is necessarily the high point on the tangent line π_0. This suggests a more general method for finding the center of a concentric elliptical contour system. After measuring the contour tangent π_0 at some point $\mathbf{p}_0$ as before (see Fig. 5-6) one could choose *any* line parallel to π_0 and find its high point, which would be colinear with $\mathbf{p}_0$ and the center $\mathbf{x}^*$. Thus $\mathbf{x}^*$ could be found by searching along the line

---

[†] G. E. Forsythe and T. S. Motzkin, "Acceleration of the Optimum Gradient Method," Preliminary Report (abstract), *Bull. Amer. Math. Soc.*, **57** (1951), pp. 304–5.

$\mathbf{p_3}$-$\mathbf{p_0}$. This technique, which does not use gradients, is the two-dimensional version of what will be called *general partan*.

We have not as yet proven why steepest ascent partan and general partan work. To do this, consider a criterion function $y(x_1, x_2)$ of two variables whose contours are concentric ellipses centered about the point $\mathbf{x}^* \equiv (x_1^*, x_2^*)$. The general equation of such an ellipse is

$$Q(x_1, x_2) \equiv \tfrac{1}{2}a_{11}(x_1 - x_1^*)^2 + a_{12}(x_1 - x_1^*)(x_2 - x_2^*) + \tfrac{1}{2}a_{22}(x_2 - x_2^*)^2$$
$$= \text{constant} \tag{5-1}$$

where a_{11}, a_{12}, and a_{22} are constants, and $Q(x_1, x_2)$ is an abbreviation representing the homogeneous quadratic form. In Chap. 3 we pointed out that if the function is to have a peak it must be negative definite.

$$Q(x_1, x_2) < 0 \qquad \text{for all } x_1, x_2 \tag{5-2}$$

Notice that the criterion function itself does not have to be a quadratic form. To have elliptical contours it need only be a function of a quadratic form

$$y(x_1, x_2) = y[Q(x_1, x_2)]$$

For example, the error function $\exp Q(x_1, x_2)$ has elliptical contours although the function itself is certainly not quadratic. The spacing of the elliptical contours relative to each other does not affect the method of parallel tangents.

Consider a ray emanating from the center $\mathbf{x}^*$ and passing through two points $\mathbf{x}_1 \equiv (x_{11}, x_{12})$ and $\mathbf{x}_2 \equiv (x_{21}, x_{22})$. The ray has the vector equation

$$\mathbf{x}_2 - \mathbf{x}^* = \lambda(\mathbf{x}_1 - \mathbf{x}^*) \tag{5-3}$$

where λ is a constant equal to the ratio of the distance from the center to $\mathbf{x}_2$ and the corresponding distance to $\mathbf{x}_1$. The values of the quadratic forms $Q(\mathbf{x}_2)$ and $Q(\mathbf{x}_1)$ at the two points are related by

$$Q(\mathbf{x}_2) \equiv a_{11}(x_{21} - x_1^*)^2 + a_{12}(x_{21} - x_1^*)(x_{22} - x_2^*) + a_{22}(x_{22} - x_2^*)^2$$
$$= a_{11}\lambda^2(x_{11} - x_1^*)^2 + a_{12}\lambda^2(x_{11} - x_1^*)(x_{12} - x_2^*) + a_{22}\lambda^2(x_{12} - x_2^*)^2$$
$$Q(\mathbf{x}_2) = \lambda^2 Q(\mathbf{x}_1) \tag{5-4}$$

It follows that for any two points $\mathbf{x}_1$ and $\mathbf{x}_2$ colinear with the center,

$$\mathbf{x}_2 - \mathbf{x}^* = \left(\frac{Q_2}{Q_1}\right)^{\tfrac{1}{2}}(\mathbf{x}_1 - \mathbf{x}^*)$$

where $Q_i (i = 1, 2)$ is an abbreviation of $Q(\mathbf{x}_i - \mathbf{x}^*)$. If one contour Q_1 is known, then any other contour Q_2 can be constructed by magnifying the first contour radially by the factor $\sqrt{Q_2/Q_1}$. It is this radial similarity of ellipses which makes partan work.

Consider now the contour tangents at two points $\mathbf{x}_1$ and $\mathbf{x}_2$ colinear with the peak x^*. Let $x \equiv (x_1, x_2)$ be any point. By Eq. (3-13), the locus of points x on the contour tangent π_2 at x_2 must satisfy

$$\left(\frac{\partial Q_2}{\partial x_1}\right)(x_1 - x_{21}) + \left(\frac{\partial Q_2}{\partial x_2}\right)(x_2 - x_{22}) = 0$$

where the symbol $\partial Q_2/\partial x_i$ stands for the partial derivative of Q with respect to x_i, evaluated at the point x_2. Similarly, the tangent π_1, at x_1 is given by

$$\left(\frac{\partial Q_1}{\partial x_1}\right)(x_1 - x_{11}) + \left(\frac{\partial Q_1}{\partial x_2}\right)(x_2 - x_{12}) = 0$$

But by Eq. (5-4),

$$\left(\frac{\partial Q_2}{\partial x_i}\right) = \lambda^2\left(\frac{\partial Q_1}{\partial x_i}\right) \qquad \text{for } i = 1, 2 \tag{5-5}$$

Hence the equation for π_2 may be written with the same coefficients as that for π_1:

$$\left(\frac{\partial Q_1}{\partial x_1}\right)(x_1 - x_{21}) + \left(\frac{\partial Q_1}{\partial x_2}\right)(x_2 - x_{22}) = 0$$

It follows that both tangent lines have the same slope.

$$\frac{x_2 - x_{22}}{x_1 - x_{21}} = -\frac{(\partial Q_1/\partial x_1)}{(\partial Q_1/\partial x_2)} = \frac{x_2 - x_{12}}{x_1 - x_{11}}$$

This means that π_1 and π_2 are parallel. We have shown that if two points x_1 and x_2 are colinear with the center x^* of a set of elliptical contours, then their contour tangents π_1 and π_2 will be parallel.

For concentric ellipses, Eqs. (5-4) and (5-5) will hold only for points colinear with the center. Moreover, a straight line can be tangent to an ellipse only at the highest point on the line. It follows that the high points on any parallel lines will be colinear with the peak. It is this *parallel tangents* property of ellipses which justifies the general partan procedure of Fig. 5-6.

The instructions for general partan involve only parallelism of lines and unidimensional searches. Neither property is affected by scale changes or rotations of coordinates, which is important for two reasons. First it will simplify the analysis of partan in hyperspace by allowing us to work with spherical rather than elliptical contours. In addition it will make it possible to define *scale-invariant partan* whose performance will be totally insensitive to the choice of units of measurement.

5.05. Partan in space

Suppose next that the criterion of effectiveness is a function of a negative definite quadratic form depending on three variables x_1, x_2, and x_3. The contours of such a function are ellipsoids in the three-dimensional experimental region. In this situation the partan strategy is first to locate a plane containing the center and then to apply plane partan to find the center exactly. The first four steps of three-dimensional partan are exactly like a plane search. The fifth step locates a plane containing the peak x^*. The search is so conducted that when this plane is located there are already three points in it placed where they can be used for plane partan. Hence the center x^* is found at the sixth point p_6.

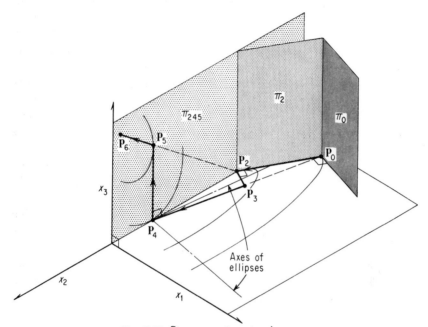

Fig. 5-7. Steep ascent partan in space.

Figure 5-7 shows an example of steep ascent partan in three dimensions. The first four steps constitute a steep ascent partan search in a plane, which for pictorial convenience has been taken to be horizontal in the isometric representation. Since the traces of the ellipsoids on any intersecting plane must be ellipses, point p_4 is where the criterion is maximum in the horizontal plane. Our intuition would suggest that the next point p_5 be located by another unidimensional search along the vertical gradient at p_4. It is important to observe that this line is parallel to the intersection of the tangent planes π_0 and π_2.

Notice that the points p_2, p_4, and p_5 are in position for an ordinary plane partan search in the plane π_{245} containing them. This is because the vertical plane π_2 tangent to p_2 intersects π_{245} in a vertical line which is necessarily parallel to the vertical line p_5-p_4. Hence by searching along the line p_5-p_2 we can find the point p_6 where the criterion is maximum in π_{245}. If we can show that the peak x^* is in this plane π_{245}, then it will follow immediately that p_6, the last point, is actually the peak. We shall do this by proving the four points p_2, p_4, p_5, and x^* to be coplanar, using the geometric proof of Shah, Buehler, and Kempthorne in their first report[†].

The coplanarity proof is accomplished by studying the behavior of general partan on spherical contours. Imagine that the original ellipsoidal contours are first rotated until their axes are parallel to those of the co-ordinate system. Then change the scales of the variables x_2 and x_3 until all three axes of the ellipsoids are equal. The contours will in this way be transformed into concentric spheres. Although the perpendicularity relations of steep ascent partan no longer hold, lines parallel before trans-formation are still parallel afterwards, and the colinearity and coplanarity of points is also preserved. Thus if p_2, p_4, p_5, and x^* are coplanar after transformation, they must have been coplanar before. Moreover, general partan is applicable in the plane π_{0234} containing the first four points, as well as in the plane π_{2456} containing p_2, p_4, p_5, and p_6.

The instructions for three-dimensional general partan, illustrated in Fig. 5-8, are: (1) Locate p_2 at the high point on any line from the arbitrary starting point p_0, making sure the line is not in the tangent plane π_0 at p_0. (2) Place p_3 at the high point on any line from p_2 parallel to π_0 but not in the tangent plane π_2 at p_2. (3) Put p_4 at the summit along the line through p_0 and p_2. (4) Locate p_5 at the high point on the *unique* line from p_4 parallel to the intersection of π_0 and π_2. (5) Place p_6 at the high point on the line from p_2 through p_5. This final point will be at the center x^* of the system of three-dimensional ellipsoids.

The advantage of using spherical contours for the sake of the proof is that the line from the center x^* to any tangent point p_i is perpendicular to the tangent plane π_i there. In particular, p_2-x^* is perpendicular to π_2, and p_4-x^* is normal to π_4. Since the line p_2-p_0 is in both these planes, it must also be perpendicular to the plane π_{24x^*}, which contains the points p_2, p_4, and x^*. Now the line p_5-p_4 was constructed parallel to the intersection of the tangent planes π_0 and π_2. Since π_0 is perpendicular to p_0-x^*, and π_2 is normal to p_2-x^*, this intersection will be perpendicular to the plane π_{02x^*}, which contains the line p_2-p_0. Hence p_5-p_4 must be perpendicular to p_2-p_0, which in turn implies that p_5-p_4 must be in π_{24x^*}, also perpendicular to p_2-p_0. It follows that p_5 is in π_{24x^*}, or equivalently, that x^* is in the plane π_{245}

† B. V. Shah, R. J. Buehler, and O. Kempthorne, "The Method of Parallel Tangents (PARTAN) for Finding an Optimum," Technical Report No. 2, Office of Naval Research Contract Nonr-530(05), Iowa University Statistical Laboratory, Ames, Iowa (original report of April, 1961).

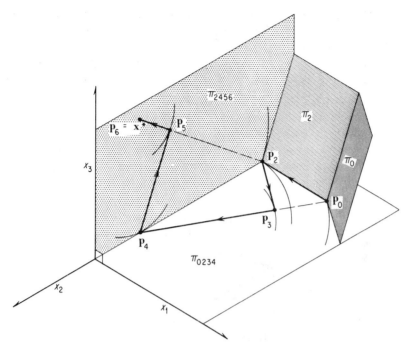

Fig. 5-8. General partan on spherical contours.

containing $\mathbf{p}_2$, $\mathbf{p}_4$, and $\mathbf{p}_5$. Since $\mathbf{p}_6$ is the highest point in π_{245}, the peak $\mathbf{x}^*$ must be at $\mathbf{p}_6$, which establishes the validity of both general and steep ascent partan.

5.06. An advantage of steep ascent

The steep ascent option has an advantage over any other version of partan. If any of the axes of the ellipsoid system are equal, steep ascent partan will reach the center sooner. This is clearly true when all of the axes are equal, for in this case the contours are spherical and the first gradient line from $\mathbf{p}_0$ passes right through $\mathbf{x}^*$, that is, $\mathbf{p}_2 = \mathbf{x}^*$.

Consider the situation when only two of the axes are equal, and the contours are ellipsoids of revolution. The first four points of a steep ascent partan search determine a plane, and the traces of the ellipsoidal contours on this plane will be ellipses centered at $\mathbf{p}_4$. Fig. 5-9, in which such a plane has been for pictorial convenience taken to be horizontal, shows that the tangent planes at $\mathbf{p}_0$ and $\mathbf{p}_2$ will be perpendicular to π_{024} when steep ascent partan is used. Any set of ellipsoids of revolution must have their contours through $\mathbf{p}_0$ and $\mathbf{p}_2$ tangent to the respective tangent planes. We can construct such a contour system by rotating the plane ellipses about the line passing through p_4 and bisecting the angle $p_0 p_4 p_2$. This line is, of course, one of the axes of the system of ellipses. Alternatively, an acceptable set of contours could be obtained by rotating the ellipses about their other axis, which is the line in π_{024} at right angles to the first axis, as shown in Fig. 5-9.

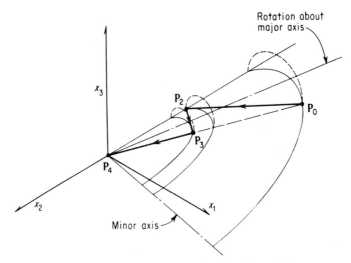

Fig. 5-9. Steep ascent partan on ellipsoids of revolution.

An ellipsoid of revolution is by definition generated by rotating an ellipse about one of its axes. No other line will do. Hence we have exhausted the number of ways that ellipsoids of revolution can be formed from the ellipses in π_{024}. It follows that p_4 is the only point which can be the center of the contour system. Therefore $p_4 = x^*$ when the ellipsoidal contours have only two axes equal.

This result can be extended to functions of any number of variables. That is, when only two axes are unequal, steep ascent partan will locate the peak after only a planar search, because the plane of the search will necessarily pass through x^*. The reason that general partan does not have this property is that the tangent planes π_0 and π_2 will not be perpendicular to π_{024} unless gradients are used to determine search directions.

5.07. Two examples of steep ascent partan

Until now our arguments have been entirely geometric, and since it may not yet be clear how to carry out the corresponding algebra, we shall study two numerical examples of steep ascent partan. The first involves maximizing $y = -2x_1^2 - x_2^2 - x_3^2$, which requires only a planar search because two of the axes are equal. The second needs a three-dimensional search because it concerns maximizing $y = -2x_1^2 - x_2^2 - 3x_3^2$, whose contours have three different axes. The functions are clearly negative definite, and their peaks are both at the origin $(0, 0, 0)$.

In the interest of simplicity and to focus attention on the search method itself the problems chosen are somewhat artificial. Generally we do not know what the function is; if we did, as in these examples, we could find the center immediately by setting the three partial derivatives of y equal to zero. However, working with a known function saves us from having to measure the slopes m_1, m_2, and m_3 of the tangent plane at a point, for in our artificial example we can obtain them simply by evaluating the partial derivatives $\partial y/\partial x_i$ $(i = 1, 2, 3)$ at the point. Thus if the coordinates of a point **a** are (a_1, a_2, a_3), the slopes for the function $-2x_1^2 - x_2^2 - x_3^2$ are $m_1 = -4a_1$, $m_2 = -2a_2$, and $m_3 = -2a_3$. The equation of the tangent plane at **a** is therefore

$$-4a_1(x_1 - a_1) - 2a_2(x_2 - a_2) - 2a_3(x_3 - a_3) = 0 \qquad (5\text{-}6)$$

where $\mathbf{x} \equiv (x_1, x_2, x_3)$ is any point in the tangent plane. In a real problem these slopes would be determined experimentally by the methods of Chap. 3.

Another convenience arising from the artificiality of the problems is that the high point on a line of search can be found by expressing the points on the line as functions of a single parameter λ (as in Chap. 3), writing the criterion function $y(y_1, x_2, x_3)$ in terms of this parameter as $y(\lambda) = y[x_1(\lambda), x_2(\lambda), x_3(\lambda)]$, and then finding the value of λ for which $dy(\lambda)/d\lambda = 0$. This technique will be illustrated in the problems. Keep in mind, however, that in an actual problem the high point would be found, not by differentiation, but by one of the unidimensional search methods of Chap. 2.

Let us begin the search for the maximum of

$$y = -2x_1^2 - x_2^2 - x_3^2$$

arbitrarily at the point $\mathbf{p}_0 = (-1, 1, -1)$. From Eq. (5-6) the equation of the tangent plane at $\mathbf{p}_0$ is

$$4(x_1 + 1) - 2(x_2 - 1) + 2(x_3 + 1) = 0$$

By Eq. (4-16) the parametric equations of the gradient line at $\mathbf{p}_0$ are

$$x_1 = -1 + 4\lambda, \qquad x_2 = 1 - 2\lambda, \qquad x_3 = -1 + 2\lambda$$

where λ is the parameter of the line. In terms of λ the criterion function y may be written

$$y = -2(-1 + 4\lambda)^2 - (1 - 2\lambda)^2 - (-1 + 2\lambda)^2$$

whence the high point can be found (artificially) by solving

$$\frac{dy}{d\lambda} = -8[2(4\lambda - 1) + (2\lambda - 1)] = 0$$

The solution is $\lambda^* = 0.3$, and

$$\mathbf{p}_2 = (-1 + 4(0.3), 1 - 2(0.3), -1 + 2(0.3)) = (0.2, 0.4, -0.4)$$

From $\mathbf{p}_2$ we again climb along the gradient, whose parametric equations are now

$$x_1 = 0.2 - 0.8\lambda, \qquad x_2 = 0.4 - 0.8\lambda, \qquad x_3 = -0.4 + 0.8\lambda$$

Along this line, $y(\lambda)$ is maximum when $\lambda^* = 0.375$, as the reader can verify. Hence

$$\mathbf{p}_3 = (-0.1, 0.1, -0.1)$$

Next comes the first acceleration step in which we search along the line from $\mathbf{p}_0$ through $\mathbf{p}_3$. The vector equation of this line is

$$\mathbf{x} - \mathbf{p}_0 = \lambda(\mathbf{p}_3 - \mathbf{p}_0)$$

whence

$$\mathbf{x} = (-1 + 0.9\lambda, 1 - 0.9\lambda, -1 + 0.9\lambda)$$

The criterion function on this line reduces to

$$y = -4(1 - 0.9\lambda)^2$$

which is clearly maximum when $\lambda^* = 10/9$.
Hence

$$\mathbf{p}_4 = (0, 0, 0)$$

In determining the tangent equation at $\mathbf{p}_4$ we find that all of the first derivatives vanish, and we are already at the peak, that is, $\mathbf{x}^* = \mathbf{p}_4$, even though a three-dimensional search ordinarily would need two more steps. This is no coincidence. The equality of two of the contour axes has made it possible to save steps by steepest ascent partan.

For the second function $y = -2x_1^2 - x_2^2 - 3x_3^2$ the peak is not found until $\mathbf{p}_6$. The gradient line at a point $\mathbf{a}$ will have the vector equation

$$\mathbf{x} = \mathbf{a} + \lambda(-4a_1, -2a_2, -6a_3)$$

Thus if we start again at $\mathbf{p}_0 = (-1, 1, -1)$, the gradient line will be described by

$$\mathbf{x} = (-1 + 4\lambda, 1 - 2\lambda, -1 + 6\lambda)$$

The maximum on this line occurs when $\lambda^* = 0.1944$, whence

$$\mathbf{p}_2 = (-0.22222, 0.61111, 0.16666)$$

The next point p_3 is located at the summit of the gradient line from p_2. We find that

$$p_3 = (0.01807, 0.28071, -0.10366)$$

The first acceleration step locates

$$p_4 = (0.1084, 0.2169, -0.0241)$$

which, as the reader can confirm, is colinear with p_0 and p_3. Since the derivatives at p_4 do not vanish, p_4 is clearly not at the peak, and so another steep ascent search must be conducted along the line

$$x = (0.1084 - 0.4337\lambda, 0.2169 - 0.4337\lambda, -0.0241 + 0.1446\lambda)$$

The summit is attained when $\lambda^* = 0.3167$, and

$$p_5 = (-0.0289, 0.0795, 0.0217)$$

The second, and in this three-dimensional case the final, acceleration step is along the line from p_2 through p_5. Since we know, in this artificial example, that $x^* = (0, 0, 0)$, let us simply verify that p_2 and p_5 are colinear with the origin, for if they are, then p_6 will be placed at x^*. By direct calculation we find that

$$p_5 = 0.130 p_2$$

which confirms that p_2 and p_5 are on the same ray from the origin. Hence

$$p_6 = x^* = (0, 0, 0)$$

5.08. Partan in hyperspace

Shah, Buehler, and Kempthorne have shown how to extend the method of parallel tangents to ellipsoidal functions of any number of independent variables. The pattern of partan is to follow each climb from a tangent plane with an acceleration step. For steep ascent partan the climb is along the gradient; for general partan it is in a direction parallel to the intersection of all preceding *even-numbered* tangent planes, including the one at the starting point p_0. The points have been numbered such that the odd-numbered ones p_3, p_5, p_7, etc. are the result of a climb, while the even-numbered ones following p_2 (that is, p_4, p_6, p_8, etc.) are obtained by acceleration. Thus in finding the maximum of a function of four variables the searcher would locate point p_6 exactly as in a three-dimensional search. Since p_6 would, however, not be at the peak when there are four dimensions, a point p_7 would be located at the summit of the line from p_6 parallel to the intersection of tangent planes π_0, π_2, and π_4. The final point p_8, at the peak of the acceleration line from p_4 through p_7, would fall at the optimum x^*.

Figure 5-10, a schematic diagram due to the inventors of partan, may help the reader picture the sequence of unidimensional searches. Contour tangent planes π_{2k} are measured at all the even numbered points $\mathbf{p}_{2k}$. ($k = 0, 1, \ldots, n - 1$, where n is the number of independent variables). The ascents from even numbered points $\mathbf{p}_{2k}$ are on lines parallel to the tangents $\pi_0, \pi_2, \ldots, \pi_{2k-2}$ ($k = 1, 2, \ldots, n - 1$). Incidentally steep ascent partan, calling as it does for gradient ascents, will automatically satisfy this parallelism requirement. The even points $\mathbf{p}_{2k}$ are determined by acceleration from $\mathbf{p}_{2k-4}$ through $\mathbf{p}_{2k-1}$ ($k = 2, 3, \ldots, n$). To start the process, $\mathbf{p}_2$ is placed at the summit of any line from the starting point $\mathbf{p}_0$. One must be careful to avoid placing the odd numbered points $\mathbf{p}_{2k-1}$ in the tangent plane π_{2k} of the preceding point $\mathbf{p}_{2k-2}$ ($k = 2, 3, \ldots, n$), for otherwise the two points would coincide. This precaution must also be taken with $\mathbf{p}_2$; it should not be in π_0. The process terminates at the point $\mathbf{p}_{2n}$ after $2n - 1$ unidimensional searches and measurement of n contour tangents, counting the last one at $\mathbf{p}_{2n}$.

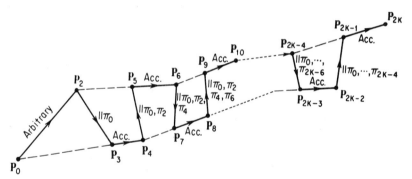

Fig. 5-10. Schematic diagram of general partan.

5.09. Scale invariant partan

The previous examples did not illustrate the algebraic interpretation of parallelism because the instruction for proceeding from even to odd points involved only the gradient. We shall give here a brief example showing how to use the partan rules for more general schemes where steep ascent is not employed. The particular technique illustrated is called *scale-invariant* partan because it will always follow the same path no matter what scales of measurement are used. All variants of general partan will find the peak at point $\mathbf{p}_{2n}$ or sooner for ellipsoidal contours, and so there would be no particular advantage to scale-invariance in this ideal case. On the other hand, the climb-and-accelerate strategy of partan could well be applied to more general contour systems, as we shall see in the next section. Under these circumstances, scale-invariance may occasionally be desirable.

Scale invariant partan involves placing the independent variables in some order. With no loss of generality we can assume for simplicity that this order will be x_1, x_2, x_3, etc. Then $\mathbf{p}_2$ is placed along the unique line from $\mathbf{p}_0$ on which all variables but x_1 are held constant. Next $\mathbf{p}_3$ is located on the line parallel to π_0 on which only x_1 and x_2 are allowed to vary. This line will also be unique because the hyperplane π_0 has $n-1$ degrees of freedom, of which $n-2$ are fixed by the requirement that x_3, x_4, ..., x_n be held constant. In general, the ascent from any even-numbered point $\mathbf{p}_{2k}$ is along the unique line parallel to $\pi_0, \pi_2, \ldots, \pi_{2k-2}$ and on which all variables but $x_1, x_2, \ldots, x_{k+1}$ are fixed. The acceleration rules are the same as for general partan.

Let us again seek the point $\mathbf{x}^*$ where the function $y = -2x_1^2 - x_2^2 - x_3^2$ is maximum, this time using scale invariant partan. As before we begin at $\mathbf{p}_0 = (-1, 1, -1)$. First we measure the tangent π_0 for future use. In this artificial example we know by Eq. (5-6) that the equation of π_0 is

$$4(x_1 + 1) - 2(x_2 - 1) + 2(x_3 + 1) = 0 \tag{5-7}$$

The next point $\mathbf{p}_2$ is to be placed along the line on which only x_1 is allowed to change. A typical point on this line would be $(x_1, 1, -1)$, and the value of the criterion would be simply $-2x_1^2 - 2$, which is obviously maximum when $x_1 = 0$. Hence

$$\mathbf{p}_2 = (0, 1, -1)$$

The next point $\mathbf{p}_3$ must be in the plane containing $\mathbf{p}_2$ and parallel to π_0. Consider any two planes whose equations are

$$m_{01}(x_1 - p_{01}) + m_{02}(x_2 - p_{02}) + m_{03}(x_2 - p_{03}) = 0 \tag{5-8a}$$

and

$$m_{21}(x_1 - p_{21}) + m_{22}(x_2 - p_{22}) + m_{23}(x_2 - p_{23}) = 0 \tag{5-8b}$$

where the m_{ij} and the p_{ij} $(i = 0, 2; j = 1, 2, 3)$ are known constants. The first plane contains the point (p_{01}, p_{02}, p_{03}); the second, (p_{21}, p_{22}, p_{23}). The two planes are parallel if and only if the corresponding slope coefficients are proportional; that is, $m_{01} = km_{21}$, $m_{02} = km_{22}$, and $m_{03} = km_{23}$ for some proportionality constant k. Hence the plane parallel to π_0 and containing $\mathbf{p}_2$ must have the equation

$$4x_1 - 2(x_2 - 1) + 2(x_3 + 1) = 0 \tag{5-9}$$

The coefficients are taken directly from Eq. (5-7). Notice that this equation is not the same as that of the tangent plane π_2 at $\mathbf{p}_2$, which is

$$-2(x_2 - 1) + 2(x_3 + 1) = 0 \tag{5-10}$$

The second condition on $\mathbf{p}_3$ is that it be in the plane $x_3 = -1$, since only x_1 and x_2 are permitted to vary. This restriction, together with Eq. (5-9) permits all points allowed to be expressed as a function of a single variable, say x_2, because

$$x_1 = \tfrac{1}{2}(x_2 - 1)$$

There being but one degree of freedom, $\mathbf{p}_3$ must lie on a line. A typical point is $(\tfrac{1}{2}(x_2 - 1), x_2, -1)$. On this line

$$y = -\tfrac{1}{2}(x_2 - 1)^2 - x_2^2 - 1$$

This function is maximum when $dy/dx_2 = 0$, which occurs when $x_2 = \tfrac{1}{3}$. Therefore

$$\mathbf{p}_3 = (-\tfrac{1}{3}, \tfrac{1}{3}, -1)$$

As usual, $\mathbf{p}_4$ is put where y is maximum on the line from $\mathbf{p}_0$ through $\mathbf{p}_3$. Points $\mathbf{x}$ on this line must satisfy

$$\mathbf{x} = \mathbf{p}_0 + \lambda(\mathbf{p}_3 - \mathbf{p}_0) = (-1, 1, -1) + \lambda(\tfrac{2}{3}, -\tfrac{2}{3}, 0)$$

The reader can verify that on this line y is maximum when $\lambda = \tfrac{3}{2}$. Hence

$$\mathbf{p}_4 = (0, 0, -1)$$

This point is the highest in the entire plane $x_3 = -1$.

Next we proceed parallel to both π_0 and π_2. From Eqs. (5-7) and (5-10) we see that such points must simultaneously satisfy

$$4x_1 - 2x_2 + 2(x_3 + 1) = 0$$

and

$$-2x_2 + 2(x_3 + 1) = 0$$

There being two equations in three unknowns, the system has but one degree of freedom and therefore describes a line in space. This time we must permit all three coordinates to vary, since by fixing any of them we would lose our only degree of freedom. Let us elect to express x_1 and x_2 in terms of x_3. Clearly $x_1 = 0$ and $x_2 = x_3 + 1$. On this line the criterion y is $-(x_3 + 1)^2 - x_3^2$, which is maximum when $x_3 = -\tfrac{1}{2}$. Therefore

$$\mathbf{p}_5 = (0, \tfrac{1}{2}, -\tfrac{1}{2})$$

Finally point $\mathbf{p}_6$ is located on the line from $\mathbf{p}_2 = (0, 1, -1)$ and $\mathbf{p}_5$. There points being obviously colinear with the origin, we know immediately that

$$\mathbf{p}_6 = (0, 0, 0) = \mathbf{x}^*$$

as we would expect.

Let us close this section by writing the general algebraic equations which each odd-numbered point $\mathbf{p}_{2k+1}$ must satisfy ($k = 1, 2, \ldots, n-1$).

Let the equation of the typical even-numbered tangent plane π_{2j} $(j = 0, 1,$ $2, \ldots, k-1)$ be

$$\sum_{l=1}^{n} m_{(2j)l}(x_l - p_{(2j)l}) = 0 \tag{5-11}$$

where the $m_{(2j)l}$ are the slope coefficients of π_{2j} and the $p_{(2j)l}$ are the co-ordinates of p_{2j}. Equations (5-8a) and (5-8b) are special cases of Eq. (5-11) for $j = 0$ and $j = 1$ respectively. Notice that the summation runs up to n, the number of independent variables. Thus Eq. (5-11) holds in hyperspace. The line from $\mathbf{p}_{2k}$, in order to be parallel to $\pi_0, \pi_2, \ldots, \pi_{2k-2}$, must satisfy the following k equations in n unknowns:

$$\sum_{l=1}^{n} m_{(2j)l}(x_l - p_{(2k)l}) = 0, \qquad j = 0, 1, \ldots, k-1 \tag{5-12}$$

This general partan rule specifies a hyperplane of $n - k$ dimensions. Scale invariant partan requires that only the first $k + 1$ variables be free to change. This means that the other $n - (k + 1)$ variables must be fixed, leaving exactly one degree of freedom. In this way a unique line is specified.

5.10. Nonellipsoidal contours

Knowing that partan performs ideally on ellipsoidal contours, we might ask two questions. First, how will partan behave for nonellipsoidal contour systems? Secondly, are there any other types of contour for which partan will find the optimum is a fixed number of steps?

In the first place, the nature of partan's rules makes it applicable to any function. When the criterion is not ellipsoidal, the point $\mathbf{p}_{2n}$ will generally not be at the maximum, but this does not prevent starting over again using $\mathbf{p}_{2n}$ as the beginning of a new partan search. Alternatively the investigator could use all of the previous tangent planes but the oldest π_0. With this approach one would conduct the search from $\mathbf{p}_{2n}$ along the unique line parallel to $\pi_2, \pi_4, \pi_6, \ldots, \pi_{2n-2}$. In general when $k \geq n$ the rule would be to locate $\mathbf{p}_{2k+1}$ along the line from $\mathbf{p}_{2k}$ parallel simultaneously to π_{2j} for $(k - n) < j < (k - 1)$. Thus partan can be considered a strategy of alternate climbs and accelerations which can be applied to any function. If steep ascent partan were used, one would expect to get close to the optimum rapidly when the investigator is skillful (or lucky) in choosing scales of measurement that make the contours approximately spherical. Good performance would also be probable on straight ridge systems because of the numerous accelerations. And one would expect criterion functions to be approximately quadratic in the neighborhood of the optimum when, as is often the case, the Taylor expansion terms of second order dominate the higher order terms.

The second question is whether there might be nonellipsoidal functions on which partan will work perfectly. In two dimensions the answer is yes, for the parallel tangents property holds for *any* radially similar contours, as illustrated in Fig. 5-11. However, when there are three or more independent variables radial similarity is not enough. Partan operates by finding the high point on an oblique planar cross section of the original contour system. Hence a function must be radially similar on every possible cross section, or partan will not work. Ellipsoids do have this necessary property, for the intersection of an $(n-1)$-dimensional hyperplane with an n-dimensional ellipsoid will be another ellipsoid of only $n-1$ dimensions. We are unaware of any other function for which every cross-section has radially similar contours.

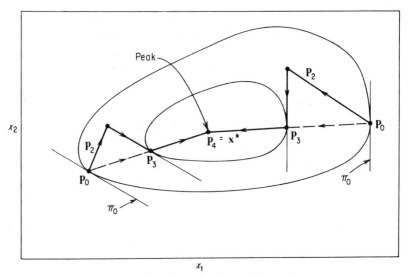

Fig. 5-11. Two dimensional partan on radially similar contours.

5.11. Summary

The method of parallel tangents alternates climbing with acceleration in a way that will find the optimum for concentric ellipsoidal contours after a small number of experiments. For a criterion function of n variables, the method ends exactly at the peak after no more than $2n-1$ unidimensional searches and n contour tangent measurements. Usable on any unimodal function, it promises to be effective in finding and following straight ridges. It is a "rich man's optimizer" in that it requires a relatively large amount of stored information and involves calculations that are far from simple. The steep ascent variant appears promising when the experimenter is able to choose scales making the contours nearly spherical. A scale-invariant option is available. The technique uses measurements of contour tangents which could conceivably be employed to eliminate regions of uncertainty when the function explored is strongly unimodal.

PATTERN SEARCH

Hooke and Jeeves[†] have devised a logical method for staying on the crest of a sharp ridge while searching for an optimum. Their *pattern search* technique is based on the hopeful conjecture that any set of moves; that is, adjustments of the independent variables, which have been successful during early experiments will be worth trying again. This strategy is successful on straight ridges because the only way an early pattern of moves can succeed is if it lies along the crest. Hence further moves in the same direction will be worthwhile if the ridge is straight.

Although the method starts cautiously with short excursions from the starting point, the steps grow with repeated success. Subsequent failure indicates that shorter steps are in order, and if a change in direction is required the technique will start over again with a new pattern. In the vicinity of the peak the steps become very small to avoid overlooking any promising direction.

The pattern technique appears admirably adapted to nonlinear curve-fitting problems involving minimization of a sum of squares. D. Himmelblau, of the University of Texas, who first brought pattern search to our attention, prefers it to any other of the many minimization techniques he has used for estimating, from experimental data, the parameters of theoretical thermodynamic and chemical kinetic expressions, which are highly nonlinear. E. Blum of the Pure Oil Company has also found pattern search effective in optimization problems connected with chemical processing. Hooke and Jeeves themselves have reported success with a curve fitting problem involving neutron flux in a nuclear reactor. They found empirically that the computation time for direct search increased only as the *first* power of the number of variables. This is striking because with classical minimization techniques the computations grow with the *cube* of the dimensionality. This phenomena may be rationalized by observing that a ridge is really a one-dimensional object, since it may be characterized by a single parameter. Thus the empirically observed efficiency of pattern search may be due precisely to its ability to follow a ridge and reduce the effective dimensionality of the problem.

[†] R. Hooke and T. A. Jeeves, " 'Direct Search' Solution of Numerical and Statistical Problems," *J. Assoc. Comp. Mach.*, **8**, 2 (April 1961), pp. 212-29.

The approach is mechanized in the "Opcon" device, developed by the Westinghouse Corporation, which has been applied to the automatic optimization of a Dow Chemical Co. pilot plant for making the chemical styrene by catalytic dehydrogenation of ethylbenzene.[†] Opcon could vary, within limits, any pair of the independent variables among heating rate (steam flow), reactor temperature, or ethylbenzene feed rate. The styrene production, as measured by refractometer, was to be maximized. The same machine has been used to optimize operation of a distillation column.[‡] Elliott Automation Ltd. has developed a similar device called "optimat."[§]

5.12. Establishing a pattern

In visualizing what is meant by a "pattern" it is helpful to think of an arrow, its base at one end and its head at the other. The search begins at a base point $\mathbf{b}_1$ which may be chosen arbitrarily; as yet the pattern has not been established. The experimenter chooses a step size δ_i for each independent variable x_i $(i = 1, 2, \ldots, k)$. Let $\boldsymbol{\delta}_i$ be the vector whose ith component is δ_i, all the rest being zero. After measuring the criterion at the initial base $\mathbf{b}_1$ one takes an observation at $\mathbf{b}_1 + \boldsymbol{\delta}_i$. If this new point is better than the base, we call $\mathbf{b}_1 + \boldsymbol{\delta}_1$ the temporary head $\mathbf{t}_{11}$, where the double subscript shows that we are developing the first pattern and that we have already perturbed the first variable x_1. Now $\mathbf{b}_1 + \boldsymbol{\delta}_1$ may not be as good as $\mathbf{b}_1$, in which case we forget $\mathbf{b}_1 + \boldsymbol{\delta}_1$ and try $\mathbf{b}_1 - \boldsymbol{\delta}_1$. If this new point is better than $\mathbf{b}_1$, we make it the temporary head; otherwise $\mathbf{b}_1$ is designated temporary head. In summary, when we are maximizing,

$$\mathbf{t}_{11} = \begin{cases} \mathbf{b}_1 + \boldsymbol{\delta}_1 & \text{if} \quad y(\mathbf{b}_1 + \boldsymbol{\delta}_1) > y(\mathbf{b}_1) & \text{(5-13a)} \\ \mathbf{b}_1 - \boldsymbol{\delta}_1 & \text{if} \quad y(\mathbf{b}_1 - \boldsymbol{\delta}_1) > y(\mathbf{b}_1) > y(\mathbf{b}_1 + \boldsymbol{\delta}_1) & \text{(5-13b)} \\ \mathbf{b}_1 & \text{if} \quad y(\mathbf{b}_1) > \max\left[y(\mathbf{b}_1 + \boldsymbol{\delta}_1), y(\mathbf{b}_1 - \boldsymbol{\delta}_1)\right] & \text{(5-13c)} \end{cases}$$

In Fig. 5-12, Eq. (5-13b) governs.

Perturbation of x_2, the next independent variable, is now carried out in a similar manner, this time about the temporary head $\mathbf{t}_{11}$ instead of the original base $\mathbf{b}_1$. In general the jth temporary head $\mathbf{t}_{1j}$ is obtained from the preceding one $\mathbf{t}_{1, j-1}$ in the following manner:

$$\mathbf{t}_{ij} = \begin{cases} \mathbf{t}_{1, j-1} + \boldsymbol{\delta}_j & \text{if} \quad y(\mathbf{t}_{1, j-1} + \boldsymbol{\delta}_j) > y(\mathbf{t}_{1, j-1}) & \text{(5-14a)} \\ \mathbf{t}_{1, j-1} - \boldsymbol{\delta}_j & \text{if} \quad y(\mathbf{t}_{1, j-1} - \boldsymbol{\delta}_j) > y(\mathbf{t}_{1, j-1}) > y(\mathbf{t}_{1, j-1} + \boldsymbol{\delta}_j) & \text{(5-14b)} \\ \mathbf{t}_{1, j-1} & \text{if} \quad y(\mathbf{t}_{1, j-1}) > \max\left[y(\mathbf{t}_{1, j-1} + \boldsymbol{\delta}_j), y(\mathbf{t}_{1, i-1} - \boldsymbol{\delta}_j)\right] \end{cases}$$
$$\text{(5-14c)}$$

[†] "Progress Report on Opcon," *Control Eng.*, **6** (Nov. 1959), p. 124.

[‡] E. A. Weiss, D. H. Archer and D. A. Burt, "Computer Sets Tower for Best Run," *Petr. Ref.*, **40**, 10 (Oct. 1961), pp. 169–74.

[§] D. A. Bell, *Intelligent Machines* (New York: Blaisdell Publishing Company, 1962), pp. 62–63.

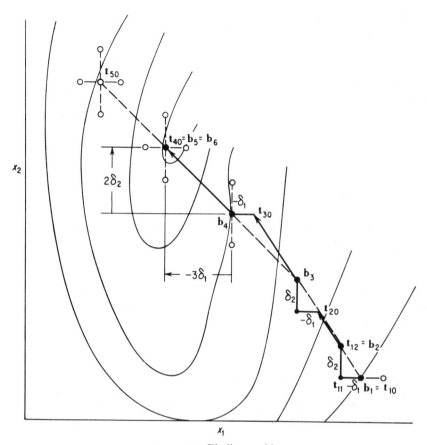

Fig. 5-12. Finding a ridge.

This expression covers all $1 < j < k$ if we adopt the convention that

$$\mathbf{t}_{10} \equiv \mathbf{b}_1$$

In Fig. 5-12, Eq. (5-14a) applies for $j = 2$. When all of the variables have been perturbed the last temporary head point $\mathbf{t}_{1k}$ is designated the *second base point* $\mathbf{b}_2$.

$$\mathbf{t}_{1k} \equiv \mathbf{b}_2$$

5.13. Pattern moves

The original base point $\mathbf{b}_1$ and the newly determined base point $\mathbf{b}_2$ together establish the first pattern. Reasoning that if a similar exploration were conducted from $\mathbf{b}_2$ the results are likely to be the same, we skip the local excursions and extend the arrow from $\mathbf{b}_1$ to $\mathbf{b}_2$ immediately, doubling its length. This establishes a new temporary head t_{20} for the second pattern based at b_2. This initial temporary head is given by

$$t_{20} \equiv b_1 + 2(b_2 - b_1) = b_2 + (b_2 - b_1) = 2b_2 - b_1$$

The double subscript 20 indicates that we are building a second pattern and that we have not yet begun to perturb the variables. A local exploration about t_{20} is now carried out to correct the tentative second pattern if necessary as shown in Fig. 5-12. The logical equations governing establishment of the new temporary heads t_{21}, t_{22}, ..., t_{2k} will be similar to Eqs. (5-14), the only difference being that the first subscript will be 2 instead of 1. The reconnaissance is completed when all of the variables have been perturbed, and the last temporary head t_{2k} is designated the third base point b_3, if, as in Fig. 5-12, the outcome there is better than at b_2.

As before, a new temporary head t_{30} is established by extrapolating from b_2 through b_3.

$$t_{30} = 2b_3 - b_2$$

In Fig. 5-12 the new base b_3 is colinear with b_2 and b_1, indicating that the direction of the pattern is not to be changed. Notice that the repeated success in this direction causes the pattern to grow, because

$$b_3 - b_2 = 2(t_{20} - b_2) = 2(b_2 - b_1)$$

The procedure is iterated for the third pattern. Suppose that perturbation of x_2 fails to produce any improvement over temporary head t_{31}, as in Fig. 5-12, but that t_{31} is still a better point than b_3. Then

$$b_4 = t_{32} = t_{31}$$

and the pattern will veer to the left, still growing in length.

For the fourth pattern imagine that none of the perturbations about the initial temporary head t_{40} improve the outcome, but that $y(t_{40}) > y(b_4)$. Then

$$b_5 = t_{42} = t_{41} = t_{40}$$

and the pattern will maintain its direction and length without any growth. The fourth pattern $b_5 - b_4$ has components $(-3 \delta_1, 2\delta_2)$, representing the cumulative effect of three successful steps in the negative x_1 direction (that is, to the left) and two in the positive x_2 direction (that is, upward).

Suppose that none of the temporary heads t_{50}, t_{51}, or t_{52} are any better than the fifth base b_5, as in Fig. 5-12. Then $b_6 = b_5$ and the pattern is destroyed. Since this could mean we are either at the peak or crossing a resolution ridge, new manuevers are in order.

5.14. Ridge tactics

Unable to continue the old pattern from b_5 even by modifying it, we must abandon it entirely and try to build a new one using b_5 as the base point but designating it b_6 since we now are working with the sixth pattern. We start all over again, making b_6 the initial temporary head t_{60} for a local exploration. If this scouting expedition locates a better point, then we can begin a new pattern. But if, as in Fig. 5-13, no better point is found then the steps must be shortened in an attempt to break the resolution ridge, if there is one. In Fig. 5-13 we have cut the steps in half and are able to obtain improvement, which starts us off on a fresh, albeit tiny pattern.

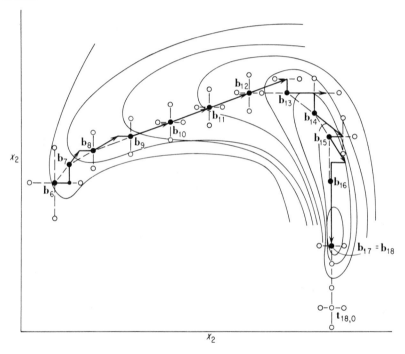

Fig. 5-13. Following a ridge.

After a few minor modifications of direction and rapid growth in size, the pattern coincides with the trend of the ridge from the ninth through eleventh pattern moves and hence holds its length constant. At b_{12} the ridge starts to curve, and the pattern swerves sharply to follow the crest, shortening up as necessary until b_{16}, where the ridge straightens out again. The sixteenth pattern lengthens rapidly on the straight ridge, but the seventeenth pattern fails to find a better point. Again the pattern must be destroyed.

5.15. Ending the search

As before we retreat to the last successful base point, in this case b_{17} (now designated b_{18}) and try to establish a nineteenth pattern by shortening up the exploratory steps. This failing to resolve the ridge, we retrench further, again with no improvement. The search terminates when the step sizes fall below a preselected minimum, as after the second reduction in Fig. 5-13. In our case, b_{17} is actually at the maximum, at least as far as we can tell with the finest resolution available.

This example shows how smoothly pattern search finds the trend of a ridge and follows it to the top. While performance of the method does not depend on the choice of scale, it certainly would be sensitive to the step size selected and the speed at which the grid is reduced to resolve a ridge.

5.16. Discrete variables

Wood[†] has pointed out that ordinary pattern search runs into difficulties when some of the variables are defined only at discrete values. This situation may be considered the multidimensional generalization of the lattice search problem discussed in Chap. 2. One can imagine many variables in a design problem which might be discrete: nominal pipe size, transformer lamination thickness, number of distillation column plates, copper wire size, or number of personnel for example.

One approach to this problem is to treat the discrete variables as if they were continuous, find the apparent optimum, and then round the discrete variables off to the nearest allowable value. While this procedure should not perform too badly for well-behaved functions, it is not yet clear just when one can rely on this approach. Moreover, it is not always practical to interpolate when a function is defined only at certain discrete values.

Lack of definition between discrete values leads to aggravation of the resolution problem, for its effect is to increase the intervals of uncertainty and broaden the resolution ridges. A search landing on such a ridge finds it difficult to establish a new pattern, for it cannot resolve the ridge by shortening its local exploration steps. Fig. 5-14 illustrates this dilemma. The variable x_1 is defined only at integral values, although x_2 is continuous.

[†] C. F. Wood, "Recent Developments in 'Direct Search' Techniques," Westinghouse Research Report 62-159-522-R1 (July, 1962).

A pattern search hits the ridge at point $\mathbf{a} = (8, 31.2)$ which is also the high point for that particular discrete value of x_1 ($= 8$). Neither points $\mathbf{b} = (9, 31.2)$ nor $\mathbf{c} = (7, 31.2)$, which are as close to $\mathbf{a}$ as possible in the x_1 direction, show any improvement over $\mathbf{b}$ and ordinary pattern search will stop in these circumstances.

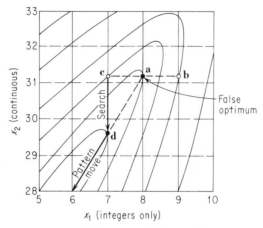

Fig. 5-14. A discrete variable problem.

Wood has suggested a way out which resembles the method of parallel tangents. He suggests moving to the nearest or most promising discrete value ($x_1 = 7$ in this case) and finding the best value of the continuous variable by a search of lower dimensionality. This new high point, at $\mathbf{d} = (7, 29.7)$ in Fig. 5-14, is used with the original point $\mathbf{a}$ to set up a pattern along the ridge. Hopefully the allowable continuous changes in the continuous pattern variables will permit correction of the pattern as needed to hold it on the ridge. Wood has had some success with this technique, although he is not yet satisfied with it because of the work required to search among the continuous variables. It would seem perhaps that the quadratic approximation methods of Secs. 3.13 through 3.16 might be justified here, at least to get the pattern going again.

5.17. Rotating coordinates

Rosenbrock[†] has devised a direct search procedure which has proved very effective at finding the minimum of the test function

$$y = 100(x_2 - x_1^2)^2 + (1 - x_1)^2 \qquad (5\text{-}15)$$

[†] H. H. Rosenbrock, "An Automatic Method for Finding the Greatest or Least Value of a Function," *Computer J.*, 3, 3 (Oct. 1960), pp. 175–84.

which has its low point at $(1, 1)$ in the shallow, curving valley shown in Fig. 5-15. The *method* of *rotating coordinates,* as we shall call it, differs from pattern search mainly in the way it carries out local explorations. Instead of perturbing each of the original variables independently as in pattern search, Rosenbrock rotates the coordinate system so that one axis points along the direction of the ridge as estimated by the previous trial. The other axes are arranged in directions normal to the first. Naturally, excursions in these normal directions are quite effective in correcting the estimate of the trend of the ridge, as indicated in Fig. 5-15.

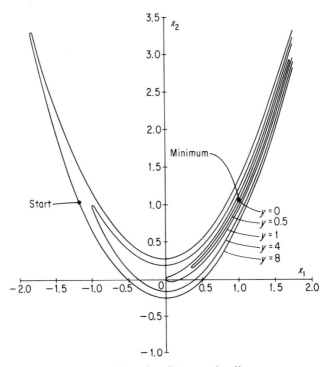

Fig. 5-15. Rosenbrock's curved valley.

Instead of taking a fixed step in each direction, Rosenbrock in effect tries to find the optimum point on each line. This procedure continuously adjusts what would in pattern search be the step size. The combined rotation of the ridge tracking vector and scale adjustment proves extremely effective on the test function. Table 5-1 shows where several schemes, all started at the point $(-1.2, 1)$, ended after 200 moves. The pattern search trials were recorded by Wood in his 1962 report.

After each set of local explorations to correct the pattern, a new set

Table 5-1

PERFORMANCE OF VARIOUS SEARCH SCHEMES AFTER 200 TRIALS
ON $y = 100(x_2 - x_1^2)^2 + (1 - x_1)^2$

Method	x_1	x_2	y
Sectioning	−0.970	0.945	3.882
Steep ascent	−0.605	0.371	2.578
Ordinary pattern	. . .	. . .	0.803
Pattern with adjusted steps	. . .	. . .	0.0103
Rotating coordinates	0.995	0.991	0.000022
Optimum	1	1	0

of coordinates must be found for determining the new search directions. We shall demonstrate how this is done for two independent variables and then give general formulae for dealing with hyperspace. Suppose that the base point $\mathbf{b}_i$ for the ith local excursion has coordinates $(2, 3)$, as in Fig. 5-16. Let the head point $\mathbf{b}_{i+1}$ for this pattern (which will be the base for the next exploration) be at $(2.4, 2.7)$. Thus one of the axes for the $(i+1)$th search should be pointed in the direction

$$(\mathbf{b}_{i+1} - \mathbf{b}_i) = (0.4, -0.3)$$

Let $\boldsymbol{\xi}_1$ be a multiple of this vector, and let us require that $\boldsymbol{\xi}_1$ have unit length relative to the scales of x_1 and x_2.

$$|\boldsymbol{\xi}_1| = 1$$

This vector is found simply by normalizing $\mathbf{b}_{i+1} - \mathbf{b}_i$, that is, by dividing each component by the total length

$$[(0.4)^2 + (0.3)^2]^{1/2} = 0.5$$

We have then that

$$\boldsymbol{\xi}_1 = (0.8, -0.6)$$

The second vector $\boldsymbol{\xi}_2$ is constructed from $\boldsymbol{\xi}_1$ and the vector $\mathbf{A}_2$ obtained from $\mathbf{b}_{i+1} - \mathbf{b}_i$ by setting the first component equal to zero.

$$\mathbf{A}_2 \equiv (0, -0.3)$$

First compute the projection of $\mathbf{A}_2$ on $\boldsymbol{\xi}_1$, shown in Fig. 5-16. This projection, also a vector, is

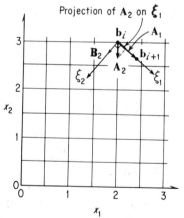

Fig. 5-16. Rotation of coordinates.

$$[(0)(0.8) + (-0.3)(-0.6)](0.8, -0.6) = (0.144, -0.108)$$

Subtraction of this projection from A_2 gives a new vector B_2 perpendicular to ξ_1, as shown in the figure.

$$B_2 = (0, -0.3) - (0.144, -0.108)$$
$$= (-0.144, -0.192)$$

The second new coordinate axis must be pointed in the same direction as B_2. Let ξ_2 be a vector of unit length in this direction. It is obtained by normalizing B_2, whose length is $[(0.144)^2 + (0.192)^2]^{1/2} = 0.240$.

$$\xi_2 = \frac{B_2}{0.240} = (-0.6, -0.8)$$

One can easily verify that ξ_1 and ξ_2 are perpendicular by comparing the slope of the former $(-\frac{3}{4})$ with that of the latter $(\frac{4}{3})$.

To develop the $(i+1)$th pattern one searches for the maximum in the ξ_1 direction. The vector equation of this line is

$$x = b_{i+1} + \lambda_1 \xi_1 = (2.4, 2.7) + \lambda_1(0.8, -0.6)$$

or in parametric form

$$x_1 = 2.4 + 0.8\lambda_1$$
$$x_2 = 2.7 - 0.6\lambda_1$$

where λ_1 is the parameter of the line of search. Suppose we find the optimum value of y on this line to be where $\lambda_1 = 2$. Then the first temporary head point for this search is at

$$t_{i+1, 1} = (4.0, 1.5)$$

From this temporary head we explore in the perpendicular direction ξ_2. The parametric equations for the search are

$$x_1 = 4.0 - 0.6\lambda_2$$
$$x_2 = 1.5 - 0.8\lambda_2$$

where λ_2 is the parameter. Suppose the optimum value of λ_2 is found to be 0.5. Then the second temporary head, which will become the next base point, is given by

$$t_{i+1, 2} = b_{i+2} = (3.7, 1.1)$$

From this point and the old base point b_{i+1}, expressed in terms of the x_1-x_2 coordinates, a new set of rotated coordinates can be calculated as before. Notice that at all times it is a simple matter to express moves in the oblique directions ξ_1 and ξ_2 in terms of the original coordinates x_1 and x_2.

When there are k independent variables, one constructs k mutually perpendicular (or *orthogonal*) vectors $\xi_1, \xi_2, \ldots, \xi_k$ from the k vectors $A_1, A_2, \ldots, A_k$, defined by

$$\mathbf{A}_1 \equiv (\mathbf{b}_{i+1} - \mathbf{b}_i) \equiv (a_1, a_2, \ldots, a_k) \tag{5-16a}$$

$$\mathbf{A}_2 \equiv (0, a_2, \ldots, a_k) \tag{5-16b}$$

$$\mathbf{A}_k \equiv (0, 0, \ldots, 0, a_k) \tag{5-16c}$$

The first is obtained by normalizing $\mathbf{A}_1$

$$\boldsymbol{\xi}_1 \equiv \frac{\mathbf{A}_1}{[\sum a_i^2]^{1/2}} \equiv (\xi_{11}, \xi_{12}, \ldots, \xi_{ik}) \tag{5-17}$$

Then one uses $\mathbf{A}_2$ to construct a vector $\mathbf{B}_2$ normal to $\boldsymbol{\xi}_1$.

$$\mathbf{B}_2 \equiv \mathbf{A}_2 - \boldsymbol{\xi}_1[\sum \xi_{1i}a_i] \equiv (b_{21}, b_{22}, \ldots, b_{2k}) \tag{5-18}$$

This is normalized to obtain $\boldsymbol{\xi}_2$.

$$\boldsymbol{\xi}_2 \equiv \frac{\mathbf{B}_2}{[\sum b_{2i}^2]^{1/2}} \equiv (\xi_{21}, \xi_{22}, \ldots, \xi_{2k}) \tag{5-19}$$

One continues in this manner, calculating $\mathbf{B}_3$, $\boldsymbol{\xi}_3$, $\mathbf{B}_4$, $\boldsymbol{\xi}_4$, etc. until at the last stage,

$$\mathbf{B}_k \equiv \mathbf{A}_k - \boldsymbol{\xi}_{k-1}[\sum \xi_{k-1,k}a_k]^{\frac{1}{2}} \equiv (b_{k1}, b_{k2}, \ldots, b_{kk}) \tag{5-20}$$

and

$$\boldsymbol{\xi}_k \equiv \frac{\mathbf{B}_k}{[\sum b_{ki}^2]^{1/2}} \tag{5-21}$$

This procedure, set forth by Rosenbrock in his article, is called the Gram-Schmidt orthogonalization process.[†] It can be used to remove interaction between variables, with the attendant advantages discussed in Secs. 1.08 and 5.01.

5.18. A poor man's ridge follower

Mugele[‡] has proposed a ridge exploration method (subprogram RIDGE of his "poor man's optimizer") which would seem to be well suited for curved ridges, although perhaps slow on the straight ones. Fig. 5-17 shows a base point $\mathbf{b}$ on a resolution ridge. Excursions in both directions have failed to produce better values of the criterion. In these circumstances subprogram RIDGE would test the point $(\mathbf{a}_1 + \mathbf{a}_2)/2$ halfway between the two points $\mathbf{a}_1$ and $\mathbf{a}_2$ already having the best results (excluding $\mathbf{b}$ itself). If the midpoint is indeed better than $\mathbf{b}$, the one-at-a-time method is resumed. On the other hand, if the midpoint fails the following quadratic approximation is tried. Let $\mathbf{a}_{12}$ be the point to be tested next. Then

[†] G. Birkhoff, and S. MacLane, *A Survey of Modern Algebra* (New York: The Macmillan Company, 1953), pp. 192–3.

[‡] R. A. Mugele, "A Nonlinear Digital Optimizing Program for Process Control Systems," *Proc. of Western Joint Computer Conf.* (1962).

$$\mathbf{a}_{12} = (1 - r)\mathbf{a}_1 + r\mathbf{a}_2 \tag{5-22}$$

where

$$r = \frac{y(\mathbf{a}_1) - y(\mathbf{a}_2)}{2\{2y[(\mathbf{a}_1 + \mathbf{a}_2)/2] - y(\mathbf{a}_1) - y(\mathbf{a}_2)\}} \tag{5-23}$$

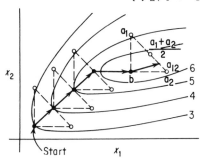

We leave to the reader the verification that this expression gives the high point of the quadratic approximation of y along the line between $\mathbf{a}_1$ and $\mathbf{a}_2$. If this new point is successful, the one-at-a-time search is renewed; otherwise one reduces the step size and starts over again. Fig. 5-17 shows how a successful search might follow a curved ridge.

Fig. 5-17. Mugele's method on a curving ridge.

5.19. Risky ridges

The ridge finding procedures discussed can be confounded, and we would be derelict in our duties it we did not point this out. The principal difficulty is that pattern search measurements are always taken in directions parallel to the coordinate axes. Since this gives no information about what is happening in other directions, it is quite possible to shorten up the local exploration steps and still miss the ridge entirely. Even Mugele's modification, which checks the point halfway between the two high points, can be led astray.

To see why this is so, consider Fig. 5-18, suggested by W. A. Graves of Colorado State University. In none of the four cases will the ridge be detected by making the pattern search grid finer. And only in Fig. 5-18a will Mugele's modification be effective the first time, although if the grid can be made fine enough it will eventually start in the right direction. We suggest therefore that the logical methods, while good at *following* ridges, may not always be as good at *finding* them. For this reason we second Box's recommendation that an experimenter always try to fit a nonlinear function in the neighborhood of any apparent optimum to make sure that many directions are searched and that one is not on a resolution ridge. Methods for doing this were discussed in Secs. 3.13 through 3.16.

5.20. Summary

Logical methods use a set of simple rules and the experience from past observations to guide the quest for an optimum. Computations for

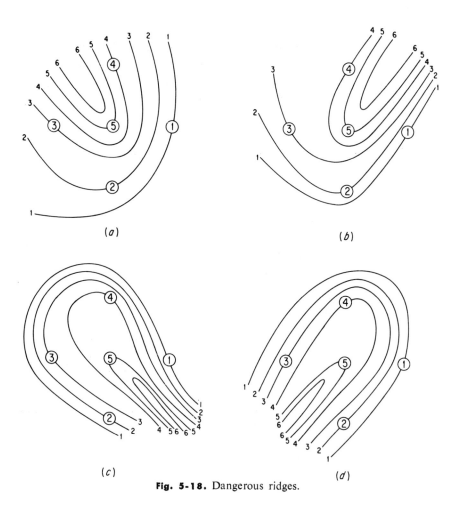

Fig. 5-18. Dangerous ridges.

these procedures are simpler than those for the geometric techniques discussed earlier. Logical methods appear to be well suited for following the long, straight ridges which seem to occur rather frequently in data smoothing and curve fitting problems. Although they can be applied to any unimodal response surface, even with some experimental error present, they do run some danger of stopping on a ridge before reaching the optimum unless the nonlinear explorations of Chap. 3 are performed.

EXERCISES

1. Use the sectioning method of Friedman and Savage to find the minimum of the following functions, starting at the point $(2, -2)$. Make no more than four searches.

    (a) $x_1^2 + 3x_2^2 + 2x_3^2$
    (b) $2x_1^2 + 2x_1x_2 + 5x_2^2$

2. Use steep ascent partan to minimize the following functions, starting at the point $(2, -2)$.

    (a) $x_1^2 + x_2^2 + x_3^2 + x_4^2$
    (b) $x_1^2 + x_2^2 + x_3^3 + 2x_4^2$
    (c) $2x_1^2 + x_2^2 + 3x_3^2$
    (d) $2x_1^4 + 2x_1^2x_2^2 + 5x_2^4$

3. Use scale invariant partan to minimize the functions of Ex. 2.

4. Use pattern search to minimize
$$y = 5x_1^2 + 6x_1x_2 + 5x_2^2 + 8x_1 + 24x_2 + 32$$
starting at the origin, setting $\delta_1 = \delta_2 = 0.1$ initially, cutting these steps in half each time the grid needs to be made finer, and stopping when no improvement is achieved with $\delta_1 = \delta_2 = 0.025$. Make no more than five pattern moves.

5. Use the method of rotating coordinates on Ex. 4, making no more than five rotations.

6. A pattern is established from the point $(5, 7, -3, 2)$ to the point $(4, 9, -2.5, 0)$. Find the four orthogonal unit vectors ξ_1, ξ_2, ξ_3, and ξ_4 which determine Rosenbrock's rotated coordinate system. If the optimal moves in these directions are respectively $2, 1, -0.5$, and 0, what are the coordinates of the next base point, expressed in terms of the original independent variables?

7. Prove Eqs. (5-22) and (5-23).

Experimental Error

6

In the preceding chapters we have either ignored or else given only cursory attention to the problem of experimental error. While this attitude is defensible when we are studying a precisely defined mathematical model, a more realistic viewpoint is in order when we face actual physical and economic systems. For in most practical situations our measurements or predictions are only *estimates,* more or less inaccurate, of the numbers in which we are interested. Because random errors of estimation cloud our perception of what is happening, they greatly hamper any search for an optimum.

In the face of "noise," a concise but apt term denoting either error of measurement or uncertainty of prediction, many of the search techniques discussed so far will not find the optimum at all. For example, a chance measurement error during a Fibonacci search easily could lead to elimination of the very section containing the optimum desired, which would of course be disastrous. "Efficiency" of a search technique means nothing unless the procedure is certain eventually to find the optimum sought. Noise forces us to consider convergence before efficiency. In this chapter we shall discuss procedures which, although capable of being confounded temporarily by random errors, will eventually migrate to the optimum.

Search techniques which successfully reach the pre-assigned goal in spite of the confusions of noise have been named *stochastic approximation procedures* by Herbert Robbins and Sutton Monro, who in 1951 devised the first scheme for finding the root of a noisy function.[†] "Approximation" refers to the continual use of past measurements to estimate the approximate position of the goal, while "stochastic" suggests the random character of the experimental errors. Shortly after publication of the pioneer work of Robbins and Monro, Kiefer and Wolfowitz adapted the idea of stochastic approximation to the problem of finding the maximum of a unimodal function obscured by noise.[‡] Their results for a function of a single variable were then extended to the multidimensional case by Blum, who used the gradient in the manner of Box and Wilson.[§] These and other early researches were unified and generalized by Dvoretzky,[‖] whose point of view will be used extensively in this chapter. An understanding of Dvoretzky's work will permit the reader to devise his own stochastic approximation schemes and prove their convergence merely by showing that the weak conditions of Dvoretzky's theorems apply. The studies of Chung,[††] Hodges and Lehman,[‡‡] and Kesten[§§] concerning speed of convergence and acceleration techniques will be reviewed to guide the reader in selecting procedures which are not only convergent but rapid as well.

6.01. Direction and distance

Stochastic approximation, much like ordinary successive approximation in the absence of experimental error, involves two basic considerations— first choosing a promising direction in which to search and then selecting the distance to travel in that direction. Picking a search direction is no more difficult for stochastic than for deterministic approximation, for one simply behaves as if he believed the experimental results, ignoring entirely the possibility of error. This means of course that the experimenter will move away from his goal whenever he is misled by the vagaries of chance

[†] H. Robbins, and S. Monro, "A Stochastic Approximation Method," *Annals of Math. Stat.*, **22** (1951), pp. 400–407.

[‡] J. Kiefer, and J. Wolfowitz, "Stochastic Estimation of the Maximum of a Regression Function," *Annals of Math. Stat.*, **23** (1952), pp. 462–66.

[§] J. R. Blum, "Multidimensional Stochastic Approximation Methods," *Annals of Math. Stat.*, **25** (1954), pp. 737–44.

[‖] A. Dvoretzky, "On Stochastic Approximation," *Proc. 3rd Berkeley Sym. on Math. Stat. and Prob.*, J. Neyman (ed.), (Berkeley: University of California Press, 1956), pp. 39–55.

[††] K. L. Chung, "On a Stochastic Approximation Method," *Annals of Math. Stat.*, **25** (1954), pp. 463–83.

[‡‡] J. L. Hodges, and E. L. Lehman, "Two Approximations to the Robbins-Monro Process," *Proc. 3rd Berkeley Sym. on Math. Stat. and Prob.*, J. Neyman (ed.) (Berkeley: University of California Press, 1956), pp. 95–104.

[§§] H. Kesten, "Accelerated Stochastic Approximation," *Annals of Math. Stat.*, **29** (1958), pp. 41–59.

error. We shall see that such temporary set-backs do not prevent ultimate convergence if the step sizes are chosen properly.

In both stochastic and deterministic approximation schemes, the corrections are made progressively smaller as the search proceeds so that the process will eventually converge. To make this convergence rapid one would like to shrink the step size as speedily as possible. The main difference between stochastic and deterministic procedures is in fact the speed with which the steps can be shortened. When noise is totally absent one can shrink the steps very rapidly, as we have seen in studying the Fibonacci technique. But when there is danger of an occasional jump in the wrong direction, shortening the steps too rapidly could make it impossible to erase the long run effects of a mistake. In such circumstances the process would still converge, but to the wrong value. We shall see that the step reduction speed is drastically limited by noise.

6.02. New data and old averages

Study of stochastic approximation will give us insight into the common problem of deciding how much influence new information should have on old practices. Our intuition tells us that if the existing way of doing things is backed by extensive experience, it should not be upset very much by new data, especially if experimental error is appreciable. On the other hand, new information should be relatively weighty in determining how to run a process only recently placed in operation. Following an idea expressed by Sheldon Chang,[†] we shall examine a special case of this problem for which we can develop a quantitative decision rule. This case and the applicable rule will help us understand the more complicated general problems to be discussed in the rest of the chapter.

Suppose we wish to estimate the output y of some system whose independent variables x_i are being held constant. Imagine that experimental error is present so that y must be estimated from n measurements z_1, z_2, ..., z_n all more or less in error. Assuming that these observations are just as likely to be too high as too low, our best estimate of y is simply the arithmetic average, denoted $\bar{z}_n$, of the n measurements.

$$\bar{z}_n \equiv \frac{1}{n} \sum_{i=1}^{n} z_i$$

Consider the relation between $\bar{z}_n$, the most recent observation z_n, and the preceding average $\bar{z}_{n-1}$ based on all but the last measurement.

[†] S. S. L. Chang, *Synthesis of Optimum Control Systems* (New York: McGraw-Hill Book Co., Inc., 1961), p. 290.

$$\bar{z}_n = \frac{(z_1 + \cdots + z_{n-1}) + z_n}{n} = \left(\frac{n-1}{n}\right)\bar{z}_{n-1} + \frac{z_n}{n}$$

We see that the old average $\bar{z}_{n-1}$ carries the weight $1\text{-}(1/n)$ while the newest observation is weighted in inverse proportion to the total number of measurements. As more and more measurements are taken the influence of new information successively decreases.

The idea of weighting new measurements in proportion to $1/n$: 1, $\frac{1}{2}$, $\frac{1}{3}$, $\frac{1}{4}$, etc. (this set of numbers is called the *harmonic sequence*) is a good rule of thumb provided it is not applied indiscriminately. A young engineer studying a manufacturing process may tend to ignore the long experience on which the operating procedures are based. If he does, he may weigh new information too heavily and in consequence suggest procedural changes that are unduly drastic. On the other hand, our analysis is based on the assumption that the true value y does not change during the sequence of measurements. If it does, then data taken before the change should not be included in the average. Managers having long experience with a particular set of operating conditions should, before defending the *status quo* too vigorously, be sure that their observations have not been made obsolete by unavoidable changes in the process.

6.03. The harmonic sequence

We shall find that the harmonic sequence 1, $\frac{1}{2}$, $\frac{1}{3}$, $\frac{1}{4}$, etc. is of central importance not only in the oversimplified situation we have just studied where the independent variables are fixed, but also in stochastic approximation schemes where operating conditions are continually being adjusted. If the step sizes are decreased according to the harmonic sequence, the procedure will eventually reach the value sought, no matter how far away it started. This is because the harmonic sequence is divergent in the sense that the sum of all of its terms is infinite.

$$\sum_{n=1}^{\infty} \frac{1}{n} = \infty \tag{6-1}$$

Sequences that shrink faster, as for example $1/n^2$: 1, $\frac{1}{4}$, $\frac{1}{9}$, $\frac{1}{16}$, etc., converge. That is, for all $p > 1$,

$$\sum_{n=1}^{\infty} \frac{1}{n^p} < \infty \tag{6-2}$$

A correction process using such a convergent sequence to weight its steps risks stopping short of the goal because its total correction effort is limited. The harmonic sequence is the fastest shrinking series of the type n^{-p} that is still divergent, that is, that has unlimited correction effort if necessary.

There is still another property of the harmonic sequence making it desirable for stochastic approximation. The sum of its *squares* is, of course, convergent, for

$$\sum_{n=1}^{\infty} \frac{1}{n^2} = 1 + \frac{1}{4} + \frac{1}{9} + \frac{1}{16} + \cdots \quad < \infty \qquad (6\text{-}3)$$

For technical reasons to be developed later, this property is important because it implies that the individual random experimental errors will tend to cancel each other out in the long run. The harmonic sequence is therefore worth remembering as a general guide to weighting together new and old data subject to random error.

FINDING A ROOT

Eventually we shall show how one can invent his own stochastic approximation methods, but before developing general principles we shall describe the first and simplest of these techniques—the Robbins-Monro method for finding a root in the presence of noise. This procedure can be adapted easily to the problem of finding an optimum, as we shall show after we have discussed the method itself.

6.04. The Robbins-Monro procedure

As in all optimization problems, we must begin by assuming some things about the function under consideration. Let there be a function y depending on a single independent variable x. For the time being let us ignore any noise and concentrate on describing the function y. Suppose it has a single root where x takes on the value $\hat{x}$. That is,

$$y(\hat{x}) = 0$$

Assume further that y is negative for all x less than $\hat{x}$ and positive for all x greater than $\hat{x}$. Then any experiment, by which we mean a measurement of y at some selected x, will tell the investigator whether he is to the right or the left of the root, and he can place his next trial in the proper direction. When the interval of uncertainty is finite the most efficient way to find the root is to put each experiment exactly in the center of the current interval, just as in the sequential dichotomous procedure described in Chap. 2. When used for finding a root this halving process is called *Bolzano's method*.[†]

Suppose now that our measurements of y are not entirely accurate.

† R. G. Stanton, *Numerical Methods for Science and Engineering* (Englewood Cliffs, N.J.: Prentice-Hall, Inc., 1961), pp. 83–84.

In this case we must distinguish between the true but unknown value y of the function and the known but probably untrue *estimate* based on our imprecise observations. Let z represent such an estimate, which is known as a *random variable* bcause even when repeated experiments are made with x held constant, the observations z will fluctuate randomly from one experiment to the next. We shall identify each experiment serially by a subscript n running from one (for the original experiment) through the natural numbers. Thus the notation $z(x_n)$ indicates the result of an experiment at some given value of x, the trial being the nth of the sequence.

The subscript emphasizes that the outcome depends not only on where the experiment was performed, but on chance as well. To see this, let x_i and x_j represent two separate trials performed at the same value of x ($x_i = x_j$ but $i \neq j$). Then although the true values of the dependent variable must be the same for both experiments $[y(x_i) = y(x_j)]$, the outcome will generally be different because of random errors $[z(x_i) \neq z(x_j)]$.

Figure 6-1 illustrates the nature of y, the random character of the observations z, and the pitfalls that await the investigator when noise interferes with his measurements. The solid line represents the underlying function y, which the statisticians would call the *regression function*. Specific observations z are shown as dots clustering around the line. The circled dots show cases where an experimenter would be misled by the chance errors into moving in the wrong direction. For instance, the four circles to the right of the root at $\hat{x}$ stand for observations which, since they are negative, would seem to the experimenter to be *left* of $\hat{x}$. One of the experiments is in fact precisely at the desired value $\hat{x}$, but its outcome, being positive instead of zero because of the noise, gives the impression that the root is farther to the right. Notice, however, that most

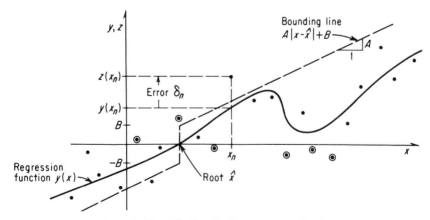

Fig. 6-1. Root finding in the presence of noise.

of the observations (the ordinary dots), although somewhat in error, would at least point the investigator in the proper direction.

6.05. Random noise

In order to deal with the noise we must make some reasonable assumptions about it. To do this we shall use several elementary concepts from probability theory which will be explained very briefly as they are introduced. More detailed discussions of these topics, already touched upon lightly in our discussion of randomization, may be found in any good text on probability or statistics.[†]

First we must assume that the observations are *unbiased*. By this we mean that for any given x, the average value of the various possible observations $z_i(x)$, each weighted by its probability density $p(z)$, would be the true value $y(x)$ at the point. This weighted average, known technically as the *expected value* of z, is defined by

$$E\{z(x)\} \equiv \int_{-\infty}^{\infty} z(x)p(z) \, dz \tag{6-4}$$

The observations are unbiased if and only if for every x it is true that

$$E\{z(x)\} \equiv y(x) \tag{6-5}$$

This assumption guarantees that the arithmetic average of any set of observations will, for fixed x, approach $y(x)$ as the sample size increases. Hence if we continue to sample long enough we can always eventually determine, for any given x, which side of the root we are on. This procedure would not be very efficient, however, and actually we shall move along the x axis after every experiment.

The other assumption concerns the variability of the observations. This variability is conventionally characterized by the *variance*, which for any given x is the expected value of the square of the deviations of the $z(x)$, measured from $y(x)$. Thus the variance $\sigma^2(x)$ at x is defined by

$$\sigma^2(x) \equiv E\{[z(x) - y(x)]^2\} \tag{6-6}$$

To ensure that the observations $z(x)$ will not often be extremely far from the true value $y(x)$, we must assume that $\sigma^2(x)$ is finite for every x. To express this precisely, let σ^2 be a finite number larger than any of the variances $\sigma^2(x)$. Then for all x we assume that

$$\sigma^2(x) < \sigma^2 < \infty \tag{6-7}$$

At any point where this condition failed to hold it would be impossible

---

[†] W. Feller, *An Introduction to Probability Theory and Its Applications* (New York: John Wiley & Sons, Inc., 1957).

to tell in which direction the root lay, no matter how many observations were taken.

The Robbins-Monro procedure involves placing experiment $n + 1$ according to the outcome of experiment n immediately preceding it. That is,

$$x_{n+1} = x_n - a_n z(x_n) \tag{6-8}$$

where a_n is one of a sequence of positive numbers which approach zero as the search progresses.

$$\lim_{n \to \infty} a_n = 0 \tag{6-9}$$

The sequence must also have the property that the sum of its elements be infinite

$$\sum_{n=1}^{\infty} a_n = \infty \tag{6-10}$$

but that the sum of the *squares* of its members be finite

$$\sum_{n=1}^{\infty} a_n^2 < \infty \tag{6-11}$$

These conditions are satisfied for example by the *harmonic sequence* $1/n$: $1, \frac{1}{2}, \frac{1}{3}, \frac{1}{4}, \ldots$, which in fact gives the fastest reduction in step size possible for sequences of the form n^{-p} without violating Eq. (6-10).

Since the adjustments are made in proportion to the value of the most recent observation, we must be sure that the regression function remains finite for finite values of x. To prevent excessive overcorrection we have to assume that y can be bounded above by a straight line on either side of the root:

$$|y| < A|x - \hat{x}| + B < \infty \tag{6-12}$$

where A and B are suitable constants. Such bounds are shown in Fig. 6-1. This requirement is not unduly restrictive in practice because one usually knows that the root lies in some finite interval, in which case one can always assume the validity of Eq. (6-12). The slope A and intercept B need not be known to establish convergence of the R-M technique, although we shall see that knowledge of the approximate value of the slope can often lead to acceleration of the search process.

6.06. Convergence

Robbins and Monro proved that when all of these not unreasonable assumptions hold, their procedure will *converge in mean square*. This technical phrase means simply that the variance of x_n, measured about the root $\hat{x}$, approaches zero as n becomes large. That is,

$$\lim_{n \to \infty} \{E[(x_n - x)^2]\} = 0 \tag{6-13}$$

Blum[†] subsequently established an even stronger form of convergence, namely that in the limit x_n is certain to equal the desired root $\hat{x}$. This *convergence with probability one* is expressed precisely by

$$P\{\lim_{n \to \infty} x_n = \hat{x}\} = 1 \qquad (6\text{-}14)$$

where the symbol $P\{\ \}$ refers to the probability of the event written between the braces. We shall see that both forms of convergence are implied by Dvoretzky's later and more general work.

6.07. Comparison of stochastic and deterministic methods

It is instructive to compare the speed of step size reduction for the stochastic R-M procedure with that for the deterministic Bolzano method.

The ratio of successive step sizes for the Bolzano halving procedure is, in absolute value, one half

$$\left| \frac{x_{n+1} - x_n}{x_n - x_{n-1}} \right| = \frac{1}{2}$$

For the R-M method this ratio depends on the dependent variable y as well as on the chance fluctuations of experimental error, so it is not possible to make a direct comparison of the ratios that will hold for all possible forms of y. One can, however, remove the random element by working with expected values. Moreover, insight into the behavior of the process can be gained by examining two extreme forms of y—one in which y remains constant for all x, and one in which y varies linearly with x. In the first case we may write

$$E\left\{ \left| \frac{x_{n+1} - x_n}{x_n - x_{n-1}} \right| \right\} = \frac{a_n}{a_{n-1}}$$

for $n = 2, 3, \ldots$. Using the harmonic sequence $1/n$ for the sequence a_n we obtain

$$E\left\{ \left| \frac{x_{n+1} - x_n}{x_n - x_{n-1}} \right| \right\} = \frac{n-1}{n} = 1 - \frac{1}{n}$$

In the second case, in which $y = Ax$, one obtains

$$E\left\{ \left| \frac{x_{n+1} - x_n}{x_n - x_{n-1}} \right| \right\} = \frac{a_n x_n}{a_{n-1} x_{n-1}} = (n-1)\frac{1 - 1/(n-1)}{n} = \frac{n-2}{n} = 1 - \frac{2}{n}$$

In both cases the ratio approaches unity from below as the process continues. Thus noise forces us to keep the step sizes fairly large, especially late in the search.

[†] J. R. Blum, "Approximation Methods which Converge with Probability One," *Annals of Math. Stat.*, **25** (1954), pp. 382–86.

The R-M root finding technique can easily be adapted to search for an optimum. Suppose we wish to find the minimum of a regression function w depending on x. Let our measurements be of dw/dx, the derivative of w with respect to x. That is, let

$$y \equiv \frac{dw}{dx}$$

Then the root of the function y corresponds to a stationary point (maximum, minimum, or inflection) for w. If y satisfies the conditions discussed in this section, then w is unimodal and has a unique minimum at x which can be found by the R-M technique. Practically speaking, however, the difficulty of measuring the slope at a point suggests that the slightly more complicated Kiefer-Wolfowitz method, specifically designed for seeking optima, will often be more effective. We shall describe the K-W procedure after we have studied stochastic approximation in more generality.

GENERAL PRINCIPLES

Now that we have seen how one stochastic approximation scheme operates, we are ready to study why it works. But rather than concentrate on the R-M method alone, we shall find it more straightforward to investigate the general case first, later specializing to specific examples.

6.08. Isolating the random component

Dvoretzky has suggested that any stochastic approximation procedure be viewed as an ordinary error-free successive approximation method with a random noise component superimposed upon it. Bertram[†] has used this idea to design adaptive control systems. We shall adopt this attitude and split off the error component so that it can be handled separately from the deterministic part. Consider for example the R-M process, Eq. (6-8),

$$x_{n+1} = x_n - a_n z(x_n)$$

The noisy observation $z(x_n)$ may be written as the sum of the true but unknown value $y(x_n)$ and an error term δ_n.

$$z(x_n) \equiv y(x_n) + \delta_n \tag{6-15}$$

Thus Eq. (6-8) becomes

$$x_{n+1} = [x_n - a_n y(x_n)] - a_n \delta_n \tag{6-16}$$

The quantity in brackets can be treated as a completely deterministic search

† J. E. Bertram, "Control by Stochastic Adjustment," *Applications and Industry* (AIEE, Jan. 1960).

scheme as far as convergence questions are concerned, and we shall use $T(x_n)$ to represent this error-free transformation; here

$$T(x_n) \equiv x_n - a_n y(x_n) \qquad (6\text{-}17)$$

All of the randomness is concentrated in the term $-a_n \delta_n$. Such random terms will be denoted in general by r_n; in this case

$$r_n \equiv -a_n \delta_n \qquad (6\text{-}18)$$

Thus the general expression for a stochastic approximation scheme is

$$x_{n+1} = T(x_n) + r_n \qquad (6\text{-}19)$$

where the specific form of the transformation $T(x_n)$ is chosen by the investigator.

It is important to perform the partitioning in such a way that the noise is unbiased, that is, its expected value is zero. This is certainly true for the R-M method by Eq. (6-5), in which we assumed unbiasedness.

$$E\{r_n\} = E\{-a_n \delta_n\} = -a_n E\{z(x_n) - y(x_n)\}$$
$$= -a_n [E\{z(x_n)\} - y(x_n)] = 0 \qquad (6\text{-}20)$$

Since the transformation $T(x_n)$ is completely error-free it would seem reasonable to study it before tackling the erratic noise term r_n. It happens, however, that the noise is so easy to handle that the problems of convergence of the deterministic part seem almost difficult by comparison. We shall therefore dispose of the noise problem first.

6.09. Noise dissipation

While noise cannot be eliminated entirely, it is sufficient for practical purposes to make the upsets caused by it suitably small. This can be accomplished by a sort of compensation process in which positive errors tend to cancel out the negative ones in the long run. To do this one must avoid shortening the steps too slowly, and our analysis of the noise problem will give a lower bound on the speed of step size reduction. We are of course more interested in the upper bound because we want to converge on the optimum as fast as possible. Still the lower bound is of some use, for occasionally we would like to shorten the steps cautiously, as when the initial estimate is likely to be quite far from the goal.

Dvoretzky has shown that to ensure convergence in mean square and with probability one, two conditions on the noise are needed. First, it must be unbiased:

$$E\{r_n\} = 0 \qquad (6\text{-}21)$$

Secondly, the sum of its variances must be finite for any possible infinite search sequence:

$$\sum_{n-1}^{\infty} E\{r_n^2\} < \infty \tag{6-22}$$

Without entering into the technicalities handled so ably by Dvoretzky, we shall indicate briefly and heuristically why these conditions are needed. We shall demonstrate how one might prove that these conditions hold in a specific case, using the R-M process as an example. Then the reader, in devising his own stochastic approximation techniques, will need only verify these conditions, leaving the rest to Dvoretzky's theorem.

In describing the R-M method we have already discussed the need for unbiased estimates. Any bias would distort our perception of the underlying regression function so that the search procedure could very well converge to the wrong point. In Eq. (6-20) the unbiasedness of the noise in the R-M process has already been demonstrated.

We like the reasoning used by Chang[†] to justify the need for finiteness of the infinite sum of variances. The cumulative error from all the noise is of course $\sum_{n=1} r_n$. If the individual errors fluctuate independently of each other, then the variance of this cumulative error is the expected value of the sum of the squared errors.

$$E\{(\sum_{n=1}^{\infty} r_n)^2\} = \sum_{n=1}^{\infty} E\{r_n^2\}$$

Suppose that this sum is finite in accordance with Eq. (6-22), and let S represent the finite sum. Now consider the situation after m trials have elapsed. The amount of variance left for the remaining experiments is

$$\sum_{n=m+1}^{\infty} E\{r_n^2\} = S - \sum_{n=1}^{m} E\{r_n^2\}$$

The second term of the right member will necessarily increase as m grows because each term of the sum is a square and therefore positive. Thus the left member must continually decrease as the search proceeds, eventually approaching zero. This behavior is desirable because it implies that the residual fluctuations will vanish in the long run. If, on the other hand, the sum in Eq. (6-22) were infinite, the disturbances would not die out.

We shall now investigate the effects of this condition on the behavior of the R-M sequence a_n. By Eq. (6-18), the variance of the cumulative error is given by

$$S = \sum_{n=1}^{\infty} E\{r_n^2\} = \sum_{n=1}^{\infty} E\{a_n^2 \delta_n^2\} = \sum_{n=1}^{\infty} a_n^2 E\{\delta_n^2\}$$

The expected value of δ_n^2, the squared error on the nth trial, is what

† S. S. L. Chang, *Synthesis of Optimum Control Systems* (New York: McGraw-Hill Book Co., Inc., 1961), pp. 289–93.

we called the error variance $\sigma^2(x_n)$ in Eq. (6-6). Robbins and Monro assume this variance to be bounded everywhere.

$$E\{\delta_n^2\} \equiv \sigma^2(x_n) < \sigma^2 < \infty \qquad (6\text{-}7)$$

Hence

$$S = \sum_{n=1}^{\infty} a_n^2 \sigma^2(x_n) < \sigma^2 \sum^{\infty} a_n^2$$

For S to be finite, it is necessary and sufficient that

$$\sum_{n=1}^{\infty} a_n^2 < \infty$$

which is precisely the condition of Eq. (6-11) required by Robbins and Monro.

As we have remarked earlier, the sum of the terms of a harmonic series is infinite, but for any sequence converging more rapidly the sum will be finite. Hence we require that

$$a_n = \frac{k_1}{n^{k_2}} \qquad (6\text{-}23a)$$

with

$$k_2 > \tfrac{1}{2} \qquad (6\text{-}23b)$$

The other constant k_1 can be any positive number. Thus the sequence $1/\sqrt{n} : 1, 1/\sqrt{2}, 1/\sqrt{3}, 1/2, 1/\sqrt{5}, \ldots$ would converge a little too slowly to dissipate the cumulative error, although any faster sequence such as $n^{-(1/2+\epsilon)}$, with $\epsilon > 0$, would be suitable.

The simple proof used here for the R-M scheme is the prototype for all stochastic approximation methods. Although it is the noise which makes the experimental problem difficult, uncertainty is not hard to handle theoretically, as we have seen. Indeed, it often takes more ingenuity to establish convergence of the deterministic component.

6.10. The deterministic component

Two situations must be considered in studying the performance of the error-free deterministic component of any stochastic approximation scheme. In the first place the trial x_n may be so close to the goal $\hat{x}$ that the next correction will overshoot and place x_{n+1} rather far on the other side of $\hat{x}$, as shown in Fig. 6-2a. On the other hand, x_n may be so far from $\hat{x}$ that there is no danger of over-correction at all, as shown in Fig. 6-2b.

To handle the first situation satisfactorily the process must be such that the maximum possible overshoot at trial n, denoted by α_n, will tend

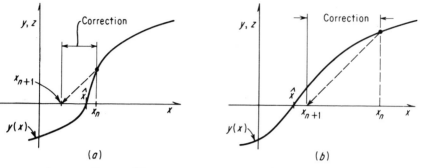

(a)   (b)

Overcorrection possible   Overcorrection impossible

Fig. 6-2. Performance of deterministic component.

to zero as n increases without limit. Thus for sufficiently large n we must
have that

$$| T(x_n) - \hat{x}| \leq \alpha_n \tag{6-24a}$$

with

$$\lim_{n \to \infty} \alpha_n = 0 \tag{6-24b}$$

When there is no possibility of overshooting we would like the distance
to the goal reduced on each trial. Let γ_n be the positive amount of reduction on the nth trial. Then the procedure should be such that

$$| T(x_n) - \hat{x}| \leq |x_n - \hat{x}| - \gamma_n \tag{6-25}$$

Although we want the restoring effect γ_n to be small when x_n is close to
$\hat{x}$, we do not want it to vanish, for if it did the process could stop moving
before it reached the goal. Thus we must require the sum of the γ_n to be
infinite.

$$\sum_{n=1}^{\infty} \gamma_n = \infty \tag{6-26}$$

With this condition on it the procedure would exert an infinite amount of
corrective effort if x_n tried to converge to any point other than $\hat{x}$.

Actually one need not always have a reduction of the distance during
the early stages of the search. Dvoretzky gives the following weaker
condition:

$$| T(x_n) - \hat{x}| \leq (1 + \beta_n)|x_n - \hat{x}| - \gamma_n \tag{6-27}$$

where β_n represents a positive fractional increase in the distance. Of course
we want β_n to vanish as the experimentation progresses, and so we require
the sum of the β_n to be finite.

$$\sum \beta_n < \infty \tag{6-28}$$

The simpler requirement of Eq. (6-25) is sufficiently weak to cover the Robbins-Monro process, in which β_n is in fact zero for all n. Using the Robbins-Monro process as an example, we shall now demonstrate how one might prove these conditions hold in a specific case.

6.11. Deterministic convergence of R-M process

In order to show that the R-M process satisfies the overshoot and restoration conditions, Dvoretzky introduced two more sequences of positive numbers ϵ_n and ρ_n, both tending to zero for large n.

$$\lim_{n \to \infty} \epsilon_n = 0 \tag{6-29}$$

$$\lim_{n \to \infty} \rho_n = 0 \tag{6-30}$$

For each trial n, ρ_n is a lower bound on the dependent variable y for all values of x_n at least ϵ_n units aways from the goal x. That is, for all x_n such that

$$|x_n - \hat{x}| > \epsilon_n \tag{6-31a}$$

it is true that

$$|y(x_n)| > \rho_n \tag{6-31b}$$

Thus when x_n is relatively far away from $\hat{x}$, we can be sure that the restoring correction will be at least $a_n \rho_n$ in absolute value. Since the sum of the a_n has been assumed infinite (Eq. (6-10)), it is easy to choose the ρ_n so that

$$\sum_{n=1}^{\infty} a_n \rho_n = \infty \tag{6-32}$$

We therefore take $a_n \rho_n$ to be the restoring effect γ_n; by Eq. (6-32) this choice satisfies condition of Eq. (6-26) that the γ_n sum to infinity. The restoration condition of Eq. (6-25) is established simply by invoking Eq. (6-31) and the definition of the R-M transformation:

$$|T(x_n) - \hat{x}| \equiv |x_n - a_n y(x_n) - \hat{x}|$$
$$= |x_n - \hat{x}| - a_n |y(x_n)| < |x_n - \hat{x}| - \gamma_n$$

Next we must consider the possibility of overshoot. Since we have chosen ϵ_n so that overcorrection is not possible for $|x_n - \hat{x}| > \epsilon_n$, we are concerned only with the situation where the adjustment procedure locates an experiment no more than ϵ_n units from $\hat{x}$.

$$|T(x_n) - \hat{x}| \le \epsilon_n$$

Since by the definition of Eq. (6-29), the sequence ϵ_n tends to zero, we could almost satisfy overshoot condition of Eq. (6-24) by taking α_n equal to ϵ_n. There is, however, the overshoot itself to be taken into account.

Overshoot occurs when the correction term $a_n y(x_n)$ exceeds the original distance $|x_n - \hat{x}|$ in absolute value. In such circumstances the R-M transformation satisfies

$$|T(x_n) - \hat{x}| = a_n|y(x_n)| - |x_n - \hat{x}|$$

Here we need to invoke the assumption that the dependent variable can be bounded linearly.

$$|y(x_n)| < A|x_n - \hat{x}| + B < \infty \tag{6-12}$$

Thus we obtain

$$|T(x_n) - \hat{x}| < (a_n A - 1)|x_n - \hat{x}| + a_n B$$

Since a_n must eventually approach zero, there is some experiment m at which $a_n A$ is less than unity. Thus for all $n \geq m$,

$$|T(x_n) - \hat{x}| < a_n B$$

The overshoot condition of Eq. (6-24) may be fulfilled by taking α_n to be either ϵ_n or $a_n B$, whichever is larger.

$$\alpha_n \equiv \max\{\epsilon_n, a_n B\}$$

Hence the R-M procedure satisfies, for sufficiently large n, the overcorrection limitation (6-24). This completes the demonstration that the R-M process satisfies the Dvoretzky conditions and therefore converges both in mean square and with probability 1 to the root $\hat{x}$.

6.12. Dvoretzky conditions

Little by little we have introduced, justified, and demonstrated Dvoretzky's conditions for convergence of a stochastic approximation scheme. It seems appropriate at this juncture to gather all of them together here in their most general form for convenient reference. It is not necessary to base the adjustments only on the most recent observation; all past measurements can be used if desired. We shall indicate this possibility by writing $T_n(x_1, \ldots, x_n)$ for the transformations.

DVORETZKY'S THEOREM. *Let α_n, β_n, and γ_n, $n = 1, 2, \ldots$, be non-negative real numbers satisfying*

(1) $\lim\limits_{n \to \infty} \alpha_n = 0$ $\hspace{6cm}$ (6-24b)

(2) $\sum\limits_{n=1}^{\infty} \beta_n < \infty$ $\hspace{6cm}$ (6-28)

(3) $\sum\limits_{n=1}^{\infty} \gamma_n = \infty$ $\hspace{6cm}$ (6-26)

Let x be a real number and T_n measurable transformations satisfying

(4) $|T_n(x_1, \ldots, x_n) - \hat{x}| \le \max \{\alpha_n, [(1 + \beta_n)|x_n - \hat{x}| - \gamma_n]\}$
for all real $x_1, \ldots, x_n$. *Let* r_n *be random variables and define*

(5) $x_{n+1} = T_n(x_1, \ldots, x_n) + r_n$ (6-19)
for $n > 0$.
   Then the conditions $E\{x_1^2\} < \infty$

(6) $\sum\limits_{n=1}^{\infty} E\{r_n^2\} < \infty$ (6-22)
and

(7) $E\{r_n\} = 0$ (6-21)
with probability 1 for all n, *imply convergence in mean square*

$$\lim_{n \to \infty} E\{(x_n - \hat{x})^2\} = 0 \qquad (6\text{-}13)$$

and convergence with probability 1.

$$P\{\lim_{n \to \infty} x_n = \hat{x}\} = 1 \qquad (6\text{-}14)$$

Dvoretzky has given us not only this powerful theorem, but also several useful generalizations of it. For instance, the sequence α_n, β_n, and γ_n need not be independent of the observations $x_1, \ldots, x_n$. Thus we can use the extension to test stochastic versions of such classic successive approximation schemes as the Newton-Raphson technique for using estimates of the first derivative to locate a root.[†] Dvoretzky also shows that bias can be tolerated as long as it tends to vanish as the experimentation proceeds. That is, the theorem holds even when condition 7 is replaced by the weaker requirement that

$$\sum_{n=1}^{\infty} E\{r_n\} < \infty \qquad (6\text{-}33)$$

for all possible sequences $x_1, \ldots, x_n$. Other generalizations of a more technical nature are given in Dvoretzky's paper.

PEAK-SEEKING

As we have shown, the R-M procedure for stochastic approximation of a root can, by a simple modification, be made to search for a maximum. This would not seem to be a very good way to carry out the search because the necessary estimation of derivatives at a point would be difficult to accomplish with any accuracy. The derivatives would be quite noisy.

6.13. The Kiefer-Wolfowitz procedure

A year after the publication of the work of Robbins and Monro, a

[†] Leon Lapidus, *Digital Computation for Chemical Engineers* (New York: McGraw-Hill Book Co., Inc., 1962), p. 288.

stochastic procedure designed specifically to find a maximum was brought out by Kiefer and Wolfowitz. Rather than estimating the derivative $y'(x_n)$ at the point x_n, they measure the dependent variable at two points a distance c_n on either side of x_n. From these two observations $z(x_n - c_n)$ and $z(x_n + c_n)$ they calculate the average slope to be

$$\frac{z(x_n + c_n) - z(x_n - c_n)}{2c_n}$$

as shown in Fig. 6-3 for a typical noisy unimodal function. From the sign of this estimated slope the most promising direction in which to locate the next pair of experiments is determined.

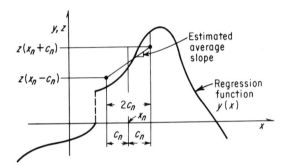

Fig. 6-3. Kiefer-Wolfowitz estimation of average slope.

The K-W procedure for locating the center x_{n+1} of the next pair of experiments may be written

$$x_{n+1} = x_n + \frac{a_n[z(x_n + c_n) - z(x_n - c_n)]}{c_n} \tag{6-34}$$

where a_n is one of a sequence of positive numbers determining the step size and c_n is the distance between the most recent pair of observations. Both the step size $2a_n$ and the span $2c_n$ vanish in the limit

$$\lim_{n \to \infty} a_n = 0 \tag{6-35a}$$

$$\lim_{n \to \infty} c_n = 0 \tag{6-35b}$$

so that the process eventually settles down. To be certain there is enough corrective action to avoid stopping short of the peak, the stepping sequence must be such that

$$\sum_{n=1}^{\infty} a_n = \infty \tag{6-36}$$

But to cancel out cumulative noise effects we must have

$$\sum_{n=1}^{\infty} \left(\frac{a_n}{c_n} \right)^2 < \infty \tag{6-37}$$

In their original article Kiefer and Wolfowitz made some additional conditions on a_n and c_n which have subsequently been proven unnecessary.

This process will converge to the maximum of a noisy unimodal function, both in mean square and with probability 1, if reasonable restrictions on the noise and on the underlying regression function y are made. Just as for the R-M process, the experimental error must be unbiased and uniformly bounded; see Eqs. (6-21) and 6-22). The condition on y is that its average slope for any pair of measurements be boundable by a straight line. That is, for all $x_1 \neq x_2$,

$$|y(x_2) - y(x_1)| < A|x_2 - x^*| + B < \infty \tag{6-38}$$

where x^* is the true location of the peak and A and B are suitable constants. This restriction, analogous to the condition of Eq. (6-12) for the R-M process, is needed to prevent excessive overshooting. It is a very weak requirement giving little trouble in practice, and even such functions as $y = -x^2$ and $y = \exp(-x^2)$ satisfy it. The proof that the K-W procedure satisfies the Dvoretzky conditions will be left to the reader, who may wish to compare his demonstration with Dvoretzky's.

6.14. Step normalization

In both procedures described so far the step size was made proportional to the magnitude of the quantity being measured—the dependent variable in the R-M scheme and the average slope in the K-W process. This idea is plausible when the measured quantities tend to increase in absolute value with distance from the goal, for in such circumstances the step sizes are large when the probability of a mistake is small and vice versa.

Figure 6-4 shows regression functions for which the conventional techniques are effective. On the right is what is known technically as a *monotonically increasing* function—one for which $y(x_2) > y(x_1)$ if and only if $x_2 > x_1$. Its root would be found quite effectively by the R-M method. The left hand illustration shows a unimodal function for which the average slope (given in Fig. 6-4(b)) is monotonically decreasing and which consequently would be suitable for the K-W technique. Such functions, said to be *concave down*, have no inflection points.

Suppose, however, that the unimodal function to be searched is only slightly more complicated, as in Fig. 6-5(a). Its average slope, given in Fig. 6-5(b), is certainly not monotonic, having as it does a minimum and a maximum corresponding to the inflection points of y. The K-W technique

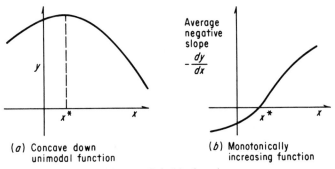

(a) Concave down   (b) Monotonically
unimodal function   increasing function

Fig. 6-4. Suitable functions.

would be very slow in the flat regions far from the maximum x^*, and as soon as it reached the steep region near the left inflection point it would jump clear over the peak into the flat region to the right. Thus it would spend most of its time slowly trying to emerge from the plains on the right, only to be thrown back again to the lowlands each time it overshot onto the cliff. This undesirable behavior was observed during some unpublished empirical studies by R. B. Cruz-Diaz at the University of Texas.

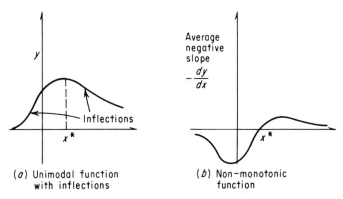

(a) Unimodal function   (b) Non-monotonic
with inflections   function

Fig. 6-5. Functions requiring normalization.

In this way any unevenness or asymmetry in a peak can confound the K-W technique and retard its speed of convergence. In such circumstances it would seem wise to use only the sign, not the magnitude, of the average slope. This *normalized* version would be written

$$x_{n+1} = x_n + a_n \, \text{sgn} \left\{ \frac{z(x_n + c_n) - z(x_n - c_n)}{2c_n} \right\} \qquad (6\text{-}39)$$

where sgn $\{u\}$ (read "signum of u") denotes the operation of taking the sign of the quantity u inside the braces. The signum operation may also be written

$$\operatorname{sgn}\{u\} \equiv \frac{u}{|u|}$$

with the convention that

$$\operatorname{sgn}\{0\} \equiv 0$$

Thus if the average slope seems to be positive, one moves a distance a_n to the right, and so on. Using the Dvoretzky theorem one can show that this normalized process converges under the same conditions as does the K-W procedure. As expected, empirical tests of the normalized technique showed it to be free from the pathological behavior discussed above. The normalized version of the R-M technique is

$$x_{n+1} = x_n - a_n \operatorname{sgn}\{z(x_n)\}$$

It should be noted that no matter how ill-behaved the regression function, it will always be concave down near the maximum. Similarly, all functions are necessarily monotonic in the neighborhood of a root. Thus unnormalized procedures regain their effectiveness near the end of a search. Functions with inflections, such as $y = \exp(-x^2)$, can often be made concave down by a logarithmic transformation $y' = \ln y$.

6.15. Acceleration

An ideal stochastic approximation scheme would take large jumps when far away from the peak, shortening its steps rapidly when approaching the goal. As we have just indicated, the unnormalized K-W procedure does this when the dependent variable is concave down.

Kesten has devised a procedure which behaves this way for more general functions and promises to bring the search in close to the goal more quickly than the unaccelerated schemes. He reasons that far from the peak there will be few reversals in the search direction because direction-finding errors will be relatively unlikely. Near the goal, however, one would expect overshooting to cause oscillation from one side to the other. Moreover the measured variable, being near zero in the neighborhood of the goal, would have its sign greatly obscured by the experimental error. Thus Kesten proposes using the number of past reversals of direction to indicate whether the search is near or far from the peak sought. One would shorten the step size only when the direction of search changes. This idea was subsequently proposed independently by Lapidus, et al.[†]

Consider, for example, Kesten's modification of the K-W technique. To be definite, suppose we are using the harmonic sequence $1, \frac{1}{2}, \frac{1}{3}, \ldots$

[†] L. Lapidus, E. Shapiro, S. Shapiro, and R. E. Stillman, "Optimization of Process Performance," *A.I.Ch.E. J.*, 7, 2 (June 1961), p. 290.

to set the step sizes, and imagine that we normalize to avoid complicating our example with considerations of the form of the dependent variable. The second line of Table 6-1 shows the signs of the average slopes measured in the course of a hypothetical search. Since we wish to find the maximum of the regression function y, the sign of the average slope also indicates the direction in which x is adjusted, a positive sign implying movement to the right. The third and fourth lines give the step sizes for the ordinary and accelerated normalized K-W schemes. Assuming in this example that the original trial x_1 is far to the left of the crest, we find that Kesten's procedure continues to use large steps until the fourth trial, when a change of sign indicates possible overshoot. Only then is the step size shortened to $\frac{1}{2}$. By this time the K-W step size has already decreased to $\frac{1}{8}$, and it is quite likely that the unaccelerated search is still quite far from the peak by this time. Sign oscillation for the Kesten search subsequently shortens the step rapidly when the peak is approached.

Table 6-1

ACCELERATED AND UNACCELERATED PEAK-SEEKING METHODS

Trial	1	2	3	4	5	6	7	8	Total Movement
Sign of observed average slope	$+$	$+$	$+$	$-$		$-$	$+$	$-$	$+$	
Unaccelerated steps	1	$\frac{1}{2}$	$\frac{1}{3}$	$-\frac{1}{4}$	$-\frac{1}{5}$	$\frac{1}{6}$	$-\frac{1}{7}$	$\frac{1}{8}$	$1\frac{149}{280}$
Accelerated steps	1	1	1	$-\frac{1}{2}$	$-\frac{1}{2}$	$\frac{1}{3}$	$-\frac{1}{4}$	$\frac{1}{5}$	$2\frac{17}{60}$

Kesten has shown that his accelerated K-W procedure converges with probability one under slightly more restrictive assumptions than the ordinary process requires. These tighter conditions are not especially bothersome in practice, and we mention them only for the sake of completeness. Kesten requires that each member of the sequence of stepping coefficients be less than all the preceding ones, that is, that

$$a_{n+1} < a_n \qquad \text{for all } n = 1, 2, 3, \ldots \qquad (6\text{-}41)$$

This condition is satisfied by the harmonic sequence anyway. The other restriction is that the distance $2c_n$ between each pair of observations be constant.

$$c_n = \text{constant} \qquad \text{for all } n = 1, 2, 3, \ldots \qquad (6\text{-}42)$$

In the ordinary K-W process this distance tends to zero in the limit.

Kesten has also given an accelerated version of the R-M procedure and shown it to converge with probability one. He has in fact proven a general theorem analogous to that of Dvoretzky in that it gives conditions under which accelerated techniques will converge with probability one.

6.16. Multidimensional extension

So far we have confined ourselves to functions of a single independent variable x. Let us turn now to the multidimensional problem in which the dependent variable y is a function of k variables $x_1, x_2, \ldots x_k$.

In the absence of experimental error the transition from one to many dimensions was rather difficult because one-dimensional problems involved powerful elimination techniques not extendable to the general case. Paradoxically, the extension is not at all painful when there is noise, precisely because the use of elimination is precluded even when there is but one independent variable. The cautious groping of the methods already studied is easy to generalize. Moreover, all the theoretical concepts needed to visualize the multidimensional problem were developed in Chaps. 3 and 4. We may therefore proceed quickly.

Two basic approaches will be developed. The first is due to Blum who has proposed a steep ascent method for multidimensional stochastic peak finding in which one searches in the direction of the gradient. The convergence proof for Blum's method can be handled by straightforward extension of Dvoretzky's theorem. A coordinate system is set up in which the point $(x_1, x_2, \ldots, x_k)$ represents a vector $\mathbf{x}$

$$\mathbf{x} \equiv (x_1, x_2, \ldots, x_k)$$

"Distance" from a point $\mathbf{x}$ to the peak $\mathbf{x}^*$, whose coordinates are $(x_1^*, x_2^*, \ldots, x_k^*)$, is defined by

$$\mathbf{x} - \mathbf{x}^* \equiv \left[\sum_{i=1}^{k} (x_i - x_i^*)^2 \right]^{\frac{1}{2}} \tag{6-43}$$

The Dvoretzky theorem still holds when the absolute values $x_n - x^*$ are replaced everywhere by the distances $|\mathbf{x}_n - \mathbf{x}^*|$. Although this definition of distance is somewhat arbitrary, depending as it does on the choice of scales, this poses no problem as long as we confine ourselves to establishing convergence. It is only when *speed* of convergence is in question that the scale difficulties discussed in Chap. 4 arise.

Suppose the experimenter has selected scales so that the problem is defined in terms of dimensionless variables. Blum estimates the slope of the tangent plane at the point $\mathbf{x}_n$ by taking observations at $\mathbf{x}_n$ and at k other points which differ from $\mathbf{x}_n$ in that exactly one of their k coordinates has been increased by c_n, the current number in the spanning sequence. Let $\mathbf{e}_j$ be the jth unit vector, whose jth coordinate is one and the rest zero.

Then the nth block of experiments requires observations at the following $k + 1$ points:

$$\mathbf{x}_n^0 = \mathbf{x}_n$$
$$\mathbf{x}_n^1 = \mathbf{x}_n + c_n\mathbf{e}_1$$
$$\mathbf{x}_n^2 = \mathbf{x}_n + c_n\mathbf{e}_2$$

$$\cdot \quad \cdot \quad \cdot \qquad\qquad (6\text{-}44)$$

$$\cdot \quad \cdot \quad \cdot$$

$$\cdot \quad \cdot \quad \cdot$$

$$\mathbf{x}_n^k = \mathbf{x}_n + c_n\mathbf{e}_k$$

This pattern of points is shown in Fig. 6-6(a).

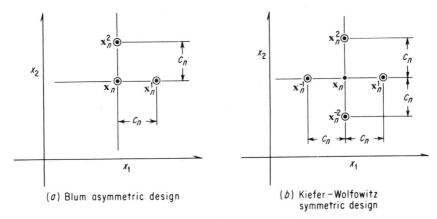

(a) Blum asymmetric design

(b) Kiefer–Wolfowitz symmetric design

Fig. 6-6. Multidimensional patterns.

For abbreviation let z_n^j be the value of the dependent variable observed at the point $\mathbf{x}_n^j$. That is,

$$z_n^j \equiv z(\mathbf{x}_n^j) \qquad j = 1, 2, \ldots, k \qquad (6\text{-}45)$$

Due to experimental error this observation will differ somewhat from the true value y_n^j of the regression function at $\mathbf{x}_n^j$. Blum's estimate of the gradient at $\mathbf{x}_n$ is simply the vector whose j^{th} component is $(z_n^j - z_n)/c_n$. The next block of experiments, whose base point is denoted $\mathbf{x}_{n+1}$, is placed in the direction of this estimated gradient. Thus if a_n is the current step size, $\mathbf{x}_{n+1}$ is given by

$$\mathbf{x}_{n+1} = \mathbf{x}_n + \frac{a_n[(z_n^1 - z_n), (z_n^2 - z_n), \ldots, (z_n^k - z_n)]}{c_n} \qquad (6\text{-}46)$$

The sequences a_n and c_n must satisfy the same conditions of Eqs. (6-35), (6-36), and (6-37) as the stepping and spanning constants for the one-dimensional K-W procedure. The regression function being explored and the experimental error must be reasonably well-behaved of course, but the restrictions placed on them are no stiffer than in the one-dimensional case. The estimated gradient must be bounded by straight planes everywhere and for every allowable spanning sequence. As usual the error variance must be finite everywhere.

Blum's method can be shown to satisfy Dvoretzky's conditions. Hence it converges to the peak $\mathbf{x}^*$ both in mean square and with probability one. Unfortunately, as Sacks has pointed out,[†] the asymmetric placement of the experiments forces them to concentrate around the wrong value, which makes the method very slow to reach the true peak. Sacks has therefore suggested a symmetric procedure which is a true multidimensional extension of the K-W method, which is itself symmetric. Sacks' extension involves making two observations for each independent variable and centering the pair about the reference point $\mathbf{x}_n$ as shown in Fig. 6-6(b). Thus in addition to the points required by Blum, Sacks would need k points defined by

$$
\begin{aligned}
\mathbf{x}_n^{-1} &= \mathbf{x}_n - c_n \mathbf{e}_1 \\
\mathbf{x}_n^{-2} &= \mathbf{x}_n - c_n \mathbf{e}_2 \\
&\quad\cdot\qquad\cdot\qquad\cdot \\
&\quad\cdot\qquad\cdot\qquad\cdot \qquad\qquad\text{(6-47)}\\
&\quad\cdot\qquad\cdot\qquad\cdot \\
\mathbf{x}_n^{-k} &= \mathbf{x}_n - c_n \mathbf{e}_k
\end{aligned}
$$

Since no measurement is necessary at $\mathbf{x}_n$ itself, Sacks would make $2k$ observations, while Blum would make only $k + 1$.

Sacks' estimate of the gradient at $\mathbf{x}_n$ is the vector whose typical component is $(z_n^j - z_n^{-j})/2c_n$. Thus his procedure is described by

$$
\mathbf{x}_{n+1} = \mathbf{x}_n + \frac{a_n[(z_n^1 - z_n^{-1}),\ (z_n^2 - z_n^{-2}),\ \ldots,\ (z_n^k - z_n^{-k})]}{2c_n} \quad \text{(6-48)}
$$

The usual conditions on the sequences, the regression function, and the error are required to shown that this procedure converges in mean square and with probability one.

SPEED OF CONVERGENCE

The conditions ensuring convergence of a stochastic approximation process are loose enough that we may well ask which particular sequence will be the best. To pose this question intelligently we must as usual define some measure of the effectiveness of a search. The concept of an

[†] Jerome Sacks, "Asymptotic Distribution of Stochastic Approximation Procedures," *Annals of Math. Stat.*, 29 (1958), pp. 397-98.

interval of uncertainty, so useful in the study of error-free search techniques, can be adapted easily to the probabilistic situation. In the absence of noise we were able to define the interval of uncertainty as that range of values of x within which the summit was known *with certainty* to lie. When there is experimental error, however, one must be satisfied with probability rather than certainty. Thus we select some satisfactorily high probability p, usually 0.95 or higher, and say that the probability is p that the peak is inside the *probabilistic interval of uncertainty*.

We shall not be concerned with this probabilistic interval of uncertainty directly. Instead we shall deal with the mean squared error $E\{(x_n - \hat{x})^2\}$ already encountered during our study of convergence. Often the mean squared error (abbreviated V_n) after n trials can be calculated even when it is impossible to establish an interval of uncertainty at all. Moreover, the size of the interval of uncertainty will increase in proportion to the square root of V_n, often called the *root mean square error*. Since our objective is not so much to know the interval of uncertainty as it is to make it as small as possible, we might just as well minimize V_n, which is much more convenient to handle.

By Eq. (6-13) we consider only those procedures for which V_n eventually vanishes.

$$\lim_{n \to \infty} V_n \equiv \lim_{n \to \infty} E\{(x_n - \hat{x})^2\} = 0 \qquad (6\text{-}49)$$

We would like sequences for which V_n not only would become as small as possible in the early stages of the search, but would approach zero rapidly in the limit. These objectives are not entirely compatible however, and the two cases will be discussed separately.

6.17. Optimal root seeking

To illustrate the considerations involved in constructing an optimal stochastic approximation procedure, we shall describe some work of Dvoretzky concerning the R-M method. Dvoretzky's result is a special case of a more general theorem of his to be discussed later because of its usefulness in the study of other procedures. As usual we shall be content to make the results plausible, referring the more advanced reader to the original article for the fine points.

Suppose we are searching for the unique root of the noisy linear functions shown in Fig. 6-7. Locating the first experiment randomly at x_1, we would place the second according to

$$x_2 = x_1 - a_1 z_1 = (x_1 - a_1 y_1) - a_1 r_1 \qquad (6\text{-}50)$$

Here the process has been partitioned into a deterministic and a random component. Let the equation of the line be given by

$$y = Ax + B \tag{6-51}$$

and assume for the sake of this argument that the slope A is known. In this rather trivial case Eqs. (6-50) and (6-51) could be combined to obtain

$$x_2 = (1 - a_1 A)x_1 - a_1 B - a_1 r_1$$

Now if a_1 were made equal to the reciprocal of the known slope A,

$$a_1 = \frac{1}{A} \tag{6-52}$$

then

$$x_2 = -\frac{B}{A} - \frac{r_1}{A}$$

Taking expectations we would have

$$E\{x_2\} = -\frac{B}{A}$$

because the noise is assumed unbiased.

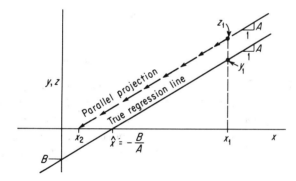

Fig. 6-7. Optimal procedure when slope is known.

The root of Eq. (6-51) being precisely $-B/A$, this choice of a_1 would center x_2 on the goal $\hat{x}$ and minimize the expected squared error V_2. This optimal procedure, illustrated in Fig. 6-7, involves running through the observation z_1 a line parallel to the regression line and locating x_2 where it intersects the x axis.

While search problems as simple as the one just discussed are not very common, it is not rare to find regression functions which can be bounded above and below by straight lines whose slopes can be estimated in advance. Such a situation, shown in Fig. 6-8, may be described mathematically by

$$0 < A_1|x - \hat{x}| \leq |y(x)| \leq A_2|x - \hat{x}| < \infty \qquad (6\text{-}53)$$

At first glance it may seem that we are estimating the location of the root $\hat{x}$, because the two straight lines must intersect on the x axis at $\hat{x}$. Notice however that we do not need to know $\hat{x}$ to estimate the slopes A_1 and A_2. These constants are in effect a priori guesses of the minimum and maximum expected adjustments which might have to be made at a given distance from the goal.

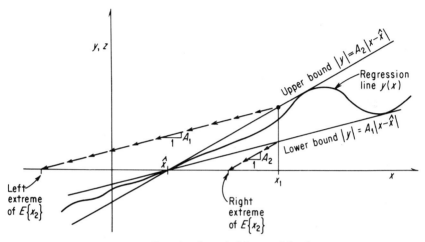

Fig. 6-8. Function bounded by straight lines.

Consider the situation at x_1. Chance determines what the error will be, but it is the experimenter who chooses the constant a_1, the reciprocal of the slope of the line projected from z, to the x axis locating x_2. To be prudent he should examine the two extreme cases that can occur—one where $y(x_1)$ is on the lower line and the other where it falls on the upper line. In the first case

$$y(x_1) = A_1(x_1 - \hat{x})$$

and hence

$$E\{x_2\} - \hat{x} = (1 - a_1A_1)(x_1 - \hat{x}) \qquad (6\text{-}54)$$

If y_1 is on the upper line, then

$$y(x_1) = A_2(x_1 - \hat{x})$$

and

$$E\{x_2\} - \hat{x} = (1 - a_1A_2)(x_1 - \hat{x}) \qquad (6\text{-}55)$$

The consequences of two extreme choices of a_1 are shown in Fig. 6-8. If a_1 is taken equal to A_2, then $E\{x_2\}$ will fall as far to the right of $\hat{x}$ as possible; similarly if $a_1 = A_1$, then $E\{x_2\}$ will be as far left as possible.

Let us be conservative and apply the minimax approach. The greatest error in $E\{x_2\}$ that can occur will be the maximum of Eqs. (6-54) and (6-55).

$$\max\{|E\{x_2\} - \hat{x}|\}$$
$$= \max\{(1 - a_1 A_1)|x_1 - \hat{x}|, (a_1 A_2 - 1)|x_1 - \hat{x}|\} \qquad (6\text{-}56)$$

We want to select a_1 so as to minimize this expression. This happens when the two terms are equal, that is when

$$1 - a_1 A_1 = a_1 A_2 - 1$$

It follows that the optimal choice is

$$a_1 = \frac{2}{A_1 + A_2} \qquad (6\text{-}57)$$

Therefore

$$\min(\max\{|E\{x_2\} - \hat{x}|\}) = \frac{A_2 - A_1}{A_1 + A_2}|x_1 - \hat{x}| \qquad (6\text{-}58)$$

Thus the minimax choice is what one would obtain simply by averaging the slopes of the boundary lines and behaving as if the regression function were a straight line with this average slope $(A_1 + A_2)/2$. Equation (6-58) is hence analogous to Eq. (6-52).

6.18. Shortening the steps

Perhaps it would be tempting to reiterate this argument and conclude that every member of the sequence of a_n should be $2/(A_1 + A_2)$. But this sequence would not satisfy Dvoretzky's theorem because the a_n would not dwindle to zero in the limit. After a moment's reflection one could see that since such a sequence would accumulate the effects of noise, the mean squared error V_n would increase without limit. It follows that for the sake of convergence we must have the subsequent a_n less than $2/(A_1 + A_2)$.

$$a_n < \frac{2}{A_1 + A_2} \qquad n = 2, 3, \ldots \qquad (6\text{-}59)$$

With this restriction on the sequence, Eq. (6-56) simplifies to

$$|E\{x_2\} - \hat{x}| \le (1 - a_1 A_1)|x_1 - \hat{x}|$$

In general we may write

$$|E\{x_{n+1}\} - \hat{x}| \le (1 - a_n A_1)|x_n - \hat{x}| \qquad n = 1, 2, 3, \ldots \qquad (6\text{-}60)$$

Now the mean squared error is given by

$$E\{(x_{n+1} - \hat{x})^2\} = E\{[(E\{x_{n+1}\} - \hat{x}) + (x_{n+1} - E\{x_{n+1}\})]^2\}$$
$$= |E\{x_{n+1}\} - \hat{x}|^2 + E\{(x_{n+1} - E\{x_{n+1}\})^2\}$$
$$= |E\{x_{n+1}\} - \hat{x}|^2 + E\{a_n^2(z_n - y_n)^2\}$$
$$= |E\{x_{n+1}\} - \hat{x}|^2 + a_n^2 E\{\delta_n^2\} \qquad (6\text{-}61)$$

where δ_n is the error on the nth trial. As in Eq. (6-7) we assume that the error variance $E\{\delta_n^2\}$ is bounded everywhere.

$$\{\delta_n^2\} < \sigma^2 < \infty \qquad (6\text{-}7)$$

Thus Eqs. (6-60), (6-61), and (6-7) may be combined to give an upper bound on the mean squared error.

$$V_{n+1} \equiv E\{(x_{n+1} - \hat{x})^2\} \le (1 - a_n A_1)^2 V_n + a_n^2 \sigma^2 \qquad (6\text{-}62)$$

It behooves the experimenter to select the value of a_n making this upper bound as small as possible. This is accomplished by setting the first derivative with respect to a_n equal to zero and solving for a_n. The result is

$$a_n = \frac{A_1 V_n}{\sigma^2 + A_1^2 V_n} \qquad (6\text{-}63)$$

This gives, when substituted into Eq. (6-62),

$$V_{n+1} \le \frac{\sigma^2 V_n}{\sigma^2 + A_1^2 V_n} \qquad (6\text{-}64)$$

Recall that the foregoing was derived under the restriction that all members of the sequence be no greater than $2/(A_1 + A_2)$. If this condition holds for the first coefficient a_1 it will be valid for all the rest, so we must be sure that the initial guess for x_1 is close enough that its mean squared error V_1 satisfies

$$a_1 = \frac{A_1 V_1}{\sigma^2 + A_1^2 V_1} \le \frac{2}{A_1 + A_2}$$

Therefore V_1 must satisfy

$$V_1 \le \frac{2\sigma^2}{A_1(A_2 - A_1)} \qquad (6\text{-}65)$$

Since

$$V_1 \equiv E\{(x_1 - \hat{x})^2\} = |x_1 - \hat{x}|^2$$

Equation (6-65) imposes the following upper bound C on the distance x_1 can be from the goal.

$$|x_1 - \hat{x}| \le C = \sqrt{\frac{2\sigma^2}{A_1(A_2 - A_1)}} \qquad (6\text{-}66)$$

In the event that the experimenter cannot say with certainty that this condition is satisfied, he should make his coefficients all $2/(A_1 + A_2)$ until he is close enough to satisfy Eq. (6-66). Treating the experiment first satisfying this condition as the initial one of a new sequence, he may then use Dvoretzky's optimal sequence.

It is convenient to express the sequence and the mean squared errors in terms of the estimated upper bound C. Taking $V_1 \leq C^2$ and iterating Eqs. (6-63) and (6-64), we obtain the sequence

$$a_n = \frac{A_1 C^2}{\sigma^2 + n A_1^2 C^2} \tag{6-67}$$

which gives the following least upper bound on the mean squared error.

$$V_n \leq \frac{\sigma^2 C^2}{\sigma^2 + (n-1)A_1 C^2} \tag{6-68}$$

The Dvoretzky sequence is minimax in the sense that no other sequence can give a smaller limit on the right member of Eq. (6-68). Only under the worst possible conditions, when $|x_1 - \hat{x}| = C$ and $|y| = A_1 |x - \hat{x}|$, will the equality signs hold in Eqs. (6-67) and (6-68).

By using Eq. (6-66) to eliminate C from Eqs. (6-67) and (6-68) we obtain

$$a_n = \frac{1}{A_1 \left[n + \left(\dfrac{A_2 - A_1}{2 A_1} \right) \right]} \tag{6-69}$$

and

$$V_n \leq \frac{\sigma^2}{A_1 \left[\dfrac{A_2 - A_1}{2} + (n-1)A_1 \right]} \tag{6-70}$$

Equation (6-69) is perhaps surprising. It shows not only that the optimal sequence is unaffected by the experimental error, but also that the sequence is not even harmonic! The effect of the noise is reflected entirely in the interval of uncertainty, as shown by Eq. (6-70). Roughly speaking, the probabilistic interval of uncertainty after each experiment is proportional to the standard deviation (root mean square) of the error.

Were A_2 to equal A_1, the Dvoretzky sequence would reduce to $1/A_1 n$ just as in the linear case which lead to Eq. (6-52). Only under these circumstances is the sequence harmonic; otherwise there is a positive constant in the denominator. When n is large, the sequence is approximately harmonic, and the slope A_2 of the upper bounding line has less and less influence on the step size. The lower line slope A_1 is always important, since in the long run the sequence behaves as if it thought the regression function were a straight line of slope A_1. If this slope A_1 is small, the mean squared deviation V_n remains large for a long time.

6.19. Asymptotic behavior

Pertinent in this connection is the work of Chung and Hodges and Lehman concerning the asymptotic behavior of ordinary harmonic sequences. They found that to make V_n small for large n it is advisable to choose

$$a_n = \frac{1}{ny'(\hat{x})} \tag{6-71}$$

where $y'(\hat{x})$ is the slope of the regression function evaluated at the root $\hat{x}$. For this choice V_n approaches $\sigma^2/n[y'(\hat{x})]^2$, which is of course less than σ^2/nA_1^2. We see then that the Dvoretzky sequence gains its short run effectiveness at the expense of long run efficiency.

In summary, we discern three stages to a search in the presence of noise. At the beginning, when we are far from the goal, a large coefficient

$$a_n = \frac{2}{A_1 + A_2} \qquad n = 1, 2, \ldots, m \tag{6-72}$$

should be used. As soon as we are close enough to establish the validity of Eq. (6-66), we should start reducing the step size according to

$$a_{m+n} = \frac{A_1 C^2}{\sigma^2 + nA_1^2 C^2} \qquad n = 1, 2, \ldots, m \tag{6-73}$$

where m is the index of the last experiment for which Eq. (6-66) cannot be assumed to hold. Finally, as the root $\hat{x}$ is approached closely one should reduce further to

$$a_{m+n} = \frac{1}{ny'(\hat{x})} \qquad n = m' + 1, m' + 2, \ldots \tag{6-74}$$

to achieve asymptotic efficiency.

6.20. Optimal peak finding

The optimal R-M root seeking method can be adapted to search for a peak in the way we have already discussed. For the sake of completeness, however, we shall indicate briefly how Dvoretzky's approach can be applied to the K-W peak finding procedure. In doing so we shall have a chance to describe Dvoretzky's technique more concisely than in the preceding section.

The key idea is to bound the regression function so as to be sure that the deterministic part of the transformation will reduce the error by a factor less than unity. That is, we want

$$|T(x_n) - \hat{x}| \leq F_n|x_n - \hat{x}| \qquad (6\text{-}75a)$$

with

$$0 \leq F_n < 1 \qquad (6\text{-}75b)$$

This permits us to write, employing the reasoning used in deriving Eq. (6-64),

$$E\{(x_{n+1} - \hat{x})^2\} \equiv V_{n+1} \leq F_n^2 V_n + \sigma_n'^2 \qquad (6\text{-}76)$$

where σ_n^2 is the variance of the noise component r_n. If factor F_n is a continuous function of the stepping sequence a_n, one can find the value of a_n minimizing the right member of the inequality simply by differentiating it. In this fashion a recursion relation connecting the successive coefficients a_n and mean squared errors V_n is obtained which can be iterated if initial conditions on a_1 and V_1 can be established.

Optimizing the ordinary K-W procedure would involve specifying not only the stepping sequence a_n, but the spanning sequence c_n as well. To our knowledge no solution to this problem has been reported in the literature, and our own attempts have not been successful because of difficulties in handling the shrinking span. We can, however, deal with the modified procedure in which the span c_n is held constant throughout the search. For the remainder of this section then we shall set $c_n = c$, a constant independent of n.

Once the regression function y and the error variance σ^2 have been bounded properly, the optimal stepping sequence a_n can be determined almost by direct comparison with the formulae of the section preceding. To emphasize the analogy and save space we shall work with the average slope y' defined by

$$y' \equiv \frac{y(x + c) - y(x - c)}{2c} \qquad (6\text{-}77)$$

We assume that the average slope lies in the cone-shaped region defined by

$$0 \leq \bar{A}_1|x - x^*| \leq |y'| \leq \bar{A}_2|x - x^*| < \infty \qquad (6\text{-}78)$$

where $\bar{A}_1$ and $\bar{A}_2$ are known constants. Thus the regression function y itself is assumed to lie entirely between two parabolas whose *second* derivatives are related to the constants $\bar{A}_1$ and $\bar{A}_2$.

As in the R-M analysis, let σ^2 be an upper bound on the experimental error for a single observation z of the regression function (not its average slope). A limit $\bar{\sigma}^2$ on the variance of the error in the *observed* slope z' is given by

$$E\left\{\left[\frac{\delta(x+c)-\delta(x-c)}{2c}\right]^2\right\} \leq \frac{\sigma^2}{2c^2} \equiv \bar{\sigma} \qquad (6\text{-}79)$$

We leave it to the reader to prove to himself that if

$$|x_1 - x^*| \leq \bar{C} = \sqrt{\frac{2\bar{\sigma}^2}{\bar{A}_1(\bar{A}_2 - \bar{A}_1)}} \qquad (6\text{-}80)$$

and the stepping sequence is

$$a_n = \frac{\bar{A}_1\bar{C}^2}{\bar{\sigma}^2 + n\bar{A}_1^2\bar{C}^2} = \frac{1}{\bar{A}_1\left[n + \left(\dfrac{\bar{A}_2 - \bar{A}_1}{2\bar{A}_1}\right)\right]} \qquad (6\text{-}81)$$

then the following expression is the least upper bound on the mean squared error:

$$V_n \leq \frac{\bar{\sigma}^2\bar{C}^2}{\bar{\sigma}^2 + (n-1)\bar{A}_1\bar{C}^2} = \frac{\bar{\sigma}^2}{\bar{A}_1\left[\dfrac{\bar{A}_2 - \bar{A}_1}{2}\right] + (n-1)\bar{A}_1} \qquad (6\text{-}82)$$

Here n is the number of *pairs* of observations on y which are combined to estimate y'. The last three equations are analogous respectively to Eqs. (6-68), (6-69), and (6-70).

If there is a moral to be drawn from this study of speed of convergence, it is that the more the experimenter knows about a system, the more effectively he can search for its optimum. But is this not the principal theme of the book?

> *There in the twilight cold and gray,*
> *Lifeless, but beautiful, he lay,*
> *And from the sky, serene and far,*
> *A voice fell, like a falling star,*
> *Excelsior!*
> —Longfellow, "Excelsior,"

EXERCISES

1. Use the Robbins-Monro method to find the root of the regression function $y = x^3 + x$, starting at $x = 10$. For the stepping sequence use $a_n = 0.02/n$. To simulate experimental error r_n flip a coin when each measurement is made and add (subtract) the constant k to the calculated value of y when the coin turns up heads (tails). That is, $z_n = y(x_n) + r_n$,

$$r = \begin{cases} k & \text{if coin reads "heads"} \\ -k & \text{if coin reads "tails"} \end{cases}$$

Carry out ten adjustments, keeping track of the results. Do this for
(a) $k = 0$
(b) $k = 1$
(c) $k = 2$

2. Repeat the experiment of Ex. 1, this time employing the optimal strategy of Dvoretzky.

3. Search for the maximum of $\exp(-x^2 + x)$, using the Kiefer-Wolfowitz method with $a_n = 1/n$ and $c_n = 1/\sqrt[3]{n}$. Start at $x = 2.00$ and simulate error in the same manner as in Ex. 1, carrying out ten adjustments in all. Do this for
(a) $k = 0$
(b) $k = 0.1$
(c) $k = 0.2$

4. Repeat Ex. 3, normalizing and using Kesten acceleration.

5. Repeat Ex. 4, fixing c_n at 1.00 and using a strategy patterned after that of Dvoretzky in the root-finding case.

6. Search for the maximum of $\exp(-x_1^2 - x_2^2 + x_1 - x_2)$, using $a_n = 1/n$ and $c_n = 1/\sqrt[3]{n}$. Simulate error as usual, flipping the coin for each observation (several times per adjustment). Do this ten times for
(a) $k = 0$
(b) $k = 0.1$
(c) $k = 0.2$

7. Invent a stochastic root-finding procedure for one independent variable based on the Newton-Raphson method.

8. Prove that the procedure for Prob. 7 satisfies the Dvoretzky conditions.

9. Invent a stochastic single variable peak seeking method based on fitting a quadratic function
(a) Exactly through the most recent three measurements.
(b) By the method of least squares through the most recent four measurements.
(c) By the method of least squares through all measurements.

10. Under what conditions, if any, will the schemes of Ex. 9 converge? Prove your assertions.

Index